POST ROAD

Post Road publishes twice yearly and accepts unsolicited poetry, fiction, and nonfiction submissions. Complete submission guidelines are available at www.postroadmag.com.

Subscriptions: Individuals, $18/year; Institutions, $34/year; outside the U.S. please add $6/year for postage.

Post Road is a nonprofit 501(c)(3) corporation published by Post Road Magazine, Inc. in partnership with the Boston College Department of English. All donations are tax-deductible.

Distributed by:

Ingram Periodicals, Inc., LaVergne, TN

Printed by:

BookMasters, Mansfield, OH

Post Road was founded in New York City in 1999 by Jaime Clarke and David Ryan with the following core editors: Rebecca Boyd, Susan Breen, Hillary Chute, Mark Conway, Pete Hausler, Kristina Lucenko (1999-2003), Anne McCarty and Michael Rosovsky.

Editors Emeritus include Sean Burke (1999-2001), Jaime Clarke (1999-2008), Mary Cotton, as Publisher and Managing Editor (2004-2008), Erin Falkevitz (2005-2006), Alden Jones (2002-2005), Fiona Maazel (2001-2002), Marcus McGraw (2003-2004), Catherine Parnell, as Managing Editor (2003), Samantha Pitchel (2006-2008), and Ricco Villanueva Siasoco, as Managing Editor (2009-2010).

Cover Art:
Henry Samelson, "Streaming,"
digital drawing (painting study), dimensions variable, 2016

ISBN: 978-0-9988015-0-6

POSt roaD

Publisher
Post Road Magazine, Inc.
in partnership with the
Boston College Department
of English

Art Editor
Susan Breen

Criticism Editor
Hillary Chute

Fiction Editors
Rebecca Boyd
Mary Cotton
David Ryan

Guest Editor
Suzanne Matson

Nonfiction Editors
Josephine Bergin
Pete Hausler

Poetry Editors
Mark Conway
Anne McCarty
Nicolette Nicola
Jeffrey Shotts
Lissa Warren

Recommendations Editors
Elizabeth Bologna
Annie Hartnett
Tim Huggins
Nelly Reifler

Theatre Editor
David Ryan

Layout and Design
Josephine Bergin

Web Designer
David Ryan

Managing Editor
Christopher Boucher

Assistant Managing Editors
James Boyman
Patrick Haggerty

Copyeditor
Valerie Duff-Strautmann

Interns
Kwesi Aaron
Rachel Aldrich
Kaitlin Astrella
Olivia Bono
Maria Jose Cordova
Bailey Flynn
Jakub Frankowicz
Christopher Kabacinski
Eileen Kao
Catherine Malcynsky
Caitlin Mason
Erin McGarvey
Anna Olcott
Ermol Clearfoster Sheppard
Katia Tanner
Ross Tetzloff

Readers
Lauren Bell
Stephanie Bergman
Cara Boulton
Charlie Clements
Sara Danver
Katelyn Eelman
Brendan Flanagan
Catherine Gellene
Melissa Hanan
Lindsey Hanlon
Allison Kolar
Caitlin Lahsaiezadeh
Meaghan Leahy
Sarah MacDonald
Ilana Masad
Matthew Mazzari
Marie McGrath
Matthew Messer
Joanne Nelson
Megyn Norbut
Laura Smith
Bailey Spencer
Hannah Taylor
Cedar Warman
Natasha Yglesias
Christine Zhao
Michele Zimmerman

Table of Contents

Criticism

Recommendations

Guest Folio

Contributor Notes

Greg Ames is the author of *Buffalo Lockjaw*, a novel that won the Book of the Year Award from the New Atlantic Independent Bookseller's Association (NAIBA) and received top ranking in *The Believer's* reader survey. His work has appeared in *Best American Nonrequired Reading, McSweeney's, Southern Review, The Sun*, and *North American Review*. His collection of short stories, *Funeral Platter*, will appear in fall 2017. An assistant professor in the English department at Colgate University, he splits his time between Hamilton, NY, and Brooklyn.

Andrea Cohen's fifth collection, *Unfathoming*, was published by Four Way Books in early 2017. Other recent books include *Furs Not Mine* and *Kentucky Derby*. Her poems have appeared in *The New Yorker, The Atlantic Monthly, Poetry, The Threepenny Review*, and elsewhere. Cohen directs the Blacksmith House Poetry Series in Cambridge, Massachusetts, and the Writers House at Merrimack College.

Nancy Dickeman's poems and essays appear in *Poetry Northwest, The Seattle Review, River City, The Seattle PI, Common Dreams* and other publications. She is a recipient of a Commendation Award from the National Poetry Competition, and received her MA in Creative Writing at the University of Washington where she won an Academy of American Poets Award. Her poetry manuscript is titled *Stunned with Sugar and Fire*. She is co-founder and literary curator for a multidisciplinary exhibit addressing the atomic era, *Particles on the Wall*. Her first novel manuscript, a nuclear age story, is titled *The Wind-Scattered World*.

Sharon Dolin is the author of six poetry collections, most recently, *Manual for Living* (University of Pittsburgh Press, 2016). The recipient of a 2016 PEN/Heim Translation Fund grant, she directs and teaches in Writing About Art in Barcelona each June: www.sharondolin.com/barcelona-workshops/.

Thomas Dolinger is a PhD candidate at Harvard, where he studies modern and contemporary poetry.

Author of the short-story collection, *Don't Erase Me*, **Carolyn Ferrell** was awarded the Art Seidenbaum Award of The Los Angeles Times Book Prize and the John C. Zachiris Award given by *Ploughshares*. Her stories have been anthologized in *The Best American Short Stories of the Century* and *Children of the Night: the Best Short Stories by Black Writers, 1967 to the Present*. Ferrell teaches at Sarah Lawrence College and lives with her husband and children in New York.

Colin Fleming's fiction appears in *Commentary, Boulevard, AGNI, Cincinnati Review*, and the *VQR*, with nonfiction running in *Rolling Stone, Sports Illustrated, JazzTimes, The Atlantic*, and *The Washington Post*. He is writing a memoir, *Many Moments More: A Story About the Art of Endurance*, and a novel about a reluctant piano prodigy, *The Freeze Tag Sessions*.

Adam J. Gellings is a MFA student at Ashland University, where he studies Creative Writing. You can find his work in *Quarter After Eight, Rust + Moth*, and *The Tishman Review*.

Jennifer Genest grew up riding horses and playing in the woods of Sanford, a mill town in Southern Maine. Her story, "Ways to Prepare White Perch," won the *New Delta Review* Ryan R. Gibbs Award for Short Fiction in 2014, and was selected for the Wigleaf Top 50 (very) Short Fictions. Her story in *Post Road* was created from a scene in her novel, *The Mending Wall*, which is currently seeking publication. Jennifer's writing has been published in *The Doctor TJ Eckleburg Review, Cactus Heart, Pithead Chapel*, and elsewhere. She lives in Southern California with her husband and young daughters.

Michele Glazer's most recent book is *On Tact, & the Made Up World* (Iowa). She teaches in and directs the MFA and BFA programs at Portland State University.

Elizabeth Gold is the author of the memoir, *Brief Intervals of Horrible Sanity*. Her poems have appeared in *Field, The Gettysburg Review, Guernica, Meridian* and other journals, as well as on Poetry Daily. A former New Yorker, she currently lives in Bristol, UK.

Tanya Grae is a PhD candidate at Florida State University and holds an MFA from Bennington College. She has won an Academy of American Poets Prize, and most recently, the 2016 Tennessee Williams/New Orleans Literary Festival Poetry Prize (selected by Yusef Komunyakaa). Her chapbook, *Little Wekiva River* (Five Oaks Press), is forthcoming, and her recent poems have appeared in *AGNI, New South, The Los Angeles Review, The Adroit Journal* and *The Florida Review*. Find out more at: tanyagrae.com

Nicole Haroutunian is the author of *Speed Dreaming* (Little A, 2015). She is co-founder of the reading series *Halfway There* and co-editor of the digital arts journal *Underwater New York*. She has an MFA from Sarah Lawrence College and lives in Woodside, Queens.

Jeffrey Harrison is the author of five full-length books of poetry, including *Incomplete Knowledge*, runner-up for the Poets' Prize in 2008, and most recently, *Into Daylight,* published by Tupelo Press in 2014 as the winner of the Dorset Prize and a finalist for the Massachusetts Book Award in 2015. A recipient of Guggenheim and NEA Fellowships, his poems have recently appeared in *Best American Poetry 2016, The Pushcart Prize Anthology, The New York Times Magazine, The Yale Review, The Hudson Review, The Kenyon Review*, and in many other journals. He lives in Massachusetts.

Michael J. Hess is a writer and filmmaker who lives in Toronto. He has regularly published in international and national journals such as *The Malahat Review, Grain, The Dalhousie Review, The Big Muddy*, and *Shenandoah*. His work has appeared in three anthologies; most recently, his essay "What Do You Wear to a Nudist Colony?" was included in *The Best Gay Stories 2016* (Lethe Press). He has twice been a finalist for The Iowa Review Awards in the nonfiction category. His films have played at the NYU Director's Series, NewFest, and the Kansas International Film Festival. For more information: hessstudios.wordpress.com

Dylan Hicks is a writer, musician, and the author of the novels *Amateurs* and *Boarded Windows*. His recordings include the forthcoming *Ad Out* and *Dylan Hicks Sings Bolling Greene*, a collection of songs written to accompany his first novel. His journalism has appeared in *The Village Voice, The New York Times, Slate, The Guardian, The Los Angeles Review of Books, The Star Tribune, Rain Taxi*, and elsewhere. He lives in Minneapolis with his wife, Nina Hale, and their son, Jackson.

Stephen Hitchcock is the executive director and chaplain of The Haven, a low-barrier day shelter and housing resource center in Charlottesville, VA. His poems have appeared in various journals and anthologies, including: *storySouth, Streetlight Magazine, Geez, Devouring the Green*, and *Back Talking on the Mountain of God*.

Major Jackson is the author of four collections of poetry, most recently *Roll Deep* (Norton: 2015), winner of the 2016 Vermont Book Award and hailed by *The New York Times Book Review* as "a remixed odyssey." He is the Richard A. Dennis Professor of English at University of Vermont.

Jess E. Jelsma holds an MFA in prose from the University of Alabama and is currently a doctoral candidate in creative writing at the University of Cincinnati. Her short stories and essays have appeared in *The Rumpus, Indiana Review, The Normal School, The Chicago Tribune*, and various other publications. She is presently at work on Anatomy of an Affair, a serialized nonfiction podcast, and can be found online at jessejelsma.com.

Matt Jones is a graduate of the University of Alabama MFA in Creative Writing Program. His work has appeared in *Okey-Panky, Slice Magazine, The Journal*, and various other publications. He and his partner are currently working on Anatomy of an Affair, a serialized nonfiction podcast. He can be found online at mattjonesfiction.com.

Joe Lewis is a nationally known artist, author, and professor of Art at the University of California, Irvine. He is President of the Noah Purifoy Foundation, and co-founding director of Fashion Moda. Lewis' artwork is exhibited widely both here and abroad. He has written for *Art in America, The LA Weekly* and *Artforum*; he has received many fellowships and awards. In 2008, the New York Foundation for the Arts named him Deutsche Bank Fellow in Photography.

Dave Madden is the author of *If You Need Me I'll Be Over There*, a story collection, and *The Authentic Animal: Inside the Odd and Obsessive World of Taxidermy*, a work of nonfiction. His shorter works have appeared in *Harper's, The Normal School, Prairie Schooner, DIAGRAM*, and elsewhere. He's received fellowships from the MacDowell Colony, the Sewanee Writers' Conference, and the Bread Loaf Writers' Conference, and currently teaches in the MFA program at the University of San Francisco.

Edward Mayes's books of poetry include *First Language* (Juniper Prize, University of Massachusetts Press) and *Works & Days* (AWP Prize in Poetry, University of Pittsburgh Press). He lives in Hillsborough, North Carolina and Cortona, Italy with his wife, the writer Frances Mayes. Their latest collaboration is *The Tuscan Sun Cookbook* (Random House).

Gail Mazur's seventh poetry collection, *Forbidden City*, was published in 2016 by University of Chicago Press. Among her earlier books of poems are *They Can't Take That Away from Me*, a finalist for the National Book Award; *Zeppo's First Wife*, winner of the Massachusetts Book Prize and finalist for *The Los Angeles Times* Book Award; and *Figures in a Landscape*. Mazur is the founding director of Cambridge's Blacksmith House Poetry Series and serves on the Writing Committee of the Fine Arts Work Center in Provincetown. She was Senior Distinguished Writer in Residence at Emerson College, and in 2017, Visiting Professor in Boston University's MFA Program.

Charles McGill, a multi-disciplinary artist who has exhibited widely, is a recipient of a 2015 Joan Mitchell Foundation Grant and a 2014 Pollock Krasner Foundation Grant. The majority of his work over the past fifteen years falls under the auspices of what the artist calls "The Artifacts from the Former Black Militant Golf and Country Club"—a conceptually-based body of work that incorporates golf bags and other objects into statements that explore race, politics, sex, and class, and is infused with satire and socio-political digs. Artist website: charlesmcgillart.com.

Rebecca McGill holds an MFA from George Mason University. She currently lives in Arlington, Virginia.

Former Richard Hugo House and Jack Straw Fellow Ross McMeekin's short stories have appeared in *Virginia Quarterly Review*, *Shenandoah*, *Redivider*, *Tin House Flash Fiction Fridays*, and elsewhere. He edits the literary journal *Spartan* and writes a weekly column for the *Ploughshares* blog.

Juan Morales is the author of the poetry collections *The Siren World*, *Friday and the Year That Followed*, and the forthcoming collection, *The Handyman's Guide to End Times*. He is a CantoMundo Fellow, the Editor of *Pilgrimage Magazine*, and an Associate Professor of English at Colorado State University-Pueblo, where he directs the Creative Writing Program and curates the SoCo Reading Series

April Ossmann is author of *Event Boundaries* (Four Way Books), and *Anxious Music* (Four Way Books) and has published her poetry widely in journals including *Colorado Review* and *Harvard Review*, and in anthologies. Her poetry awards include a 2013 Vermont Arts Council Creation Grant and a *Prairie Schooner* Readers' Choice Award. Former executive director of Alice James Books, she owns a poetry consulting business (www.aprilossmann.com), offering manuscript editing, publishing advice, tutorials, and workshops. She is a faculty editor for the low-residency MFA in Creative Writing Program at Sierra Nevada College. She lives in West Windsor, Vermont.

Halley Parry is a California born writer, currently based in Nashville. This is her first publication.

Ricardo Pau-Llosa is the author of seven books of poetry, the last five with Carnegie Mellon. His latest is *Man* (2014). He has new work in *American Poetry Review*, *Bellevue Literary Review*, *The Fiddlehead*, *Hudson Review*, *Island*, *New England Review*, *Southern Review*, *Stand*, et al. He is also an art critic and curator.

Lisa A. Phillips, a journalism professor at SUNY New Paltz, is the author of *Unrequited: Women and Romantic Obsession*.

Lia Purpura is the author of eight collections of essays, poems, and translations, most recently a collection of poems, *It Shouldn't Have Been Beautiful* (Penguin). Her awards include Guggenheim, NEA, and Fulbright Fellowships, as well as four Pushcart Prizes. *On Looking* (essays) was a finalist for the National Book Critics Circle Award. Her work appears in *The New Yorker*, *The New Republic*, *Orion*, *The Paris Review*, *The Georgia Review*, and elsewhere. She lives in Baltimore, MD and is Writer in Residence at The University of Maryland, Baltimore County.

Jessica Lee Richardson's first book, the story collection, *It Had Been Planned and There Were Guides*, is just out from Fiction Collective Two. It won the Ronald Sukenick Innovative Fiction Prize and was longlisted for the PEN/Robert W. Bingham Award. You can read some of her short fiction at www.jessicaleerichardson.com.

Matthew Salesses was adopted from Korea. His novel *The Hundred-Year Flood* was an Amazon Bestseller, Best Book of September, and Kindle First pick; an Adoptive Families Best Book of 2015; a Millions Most Anticipated of 2015; and a Best Book of the season at Buzzfeed, Refinery29, and Gawker, among others. Forthcoming are a new novel, *The Murder of the Doppelgänger*, and a collection of essays, *Own Story*.

Henry Samelson lives and works in Brooklyn, NY. He received his MFA from The School of the Museum of Fine Arts, Boston. His work has been shown at Horton/Sunday LES, Dodge Gallery, Miami MOCA, and is part of the permanent collection of The Walker Art Museum and the Decordova Museum. His work has been reviewed in *The New York Times, The Boston Globe, The Village Voice* and elsewhere.

Timothy Scott's stories have appeared in literary journals such as *The Massachusetts Review, New Orleans Review*, and *Colorado Review*, and in the anthology *Best New American Voices 2010*. Two stories received Pushcart nominations. He currently lives in Madison, Wisconsin, with his wife and two children.

Tara Skurtu is the recipient of a 2015-17 extended teaching Fulbright in Romania, a Robert Pinsky Global Fellowship, and two Academy of American Poets prizes. Her recent poems have appeared in *The Kenyon Review, Poetry Review, Poetry Wales*, and *Plume*. Tara is the author of the chapbook *Skurtu, Romania* (Eyewear Publishing 2016), and her debut poetry collection *The Amoeba Game* is forthcoming by Eyewear in 2017.

Bailey Spencer is an MFA candidate in poetry at Washington University in St. Louis. Her poems have appeared or are forthcoming in *Midwestern Gothic, Terrain.org*, and *The Shallow Ends*.

Jason Stoneking is an American poet and essayist who spends most of his time in France. He has authored six books, two feature-length screenplays, one album, and scores of untabulated ephemera. After recently completing a three-volume essay project, supported by two North American reading tours, he has returned to Paris where he is currently focused on poetry, performance art, and an ongoing epistolary project. More about Jason and his work can be found on his website at www.jasonstoneking.com.

Tom Treanor earned an MFA in fiction writing from Columbia University and has previously published literature reviews for *The Rumpus*. Originally from Northern California, he currently lives in Brooklyn, New York. This is his first published short story.

Jaclyn Van Lieu Vorenkamp holds a BA in French Literature from Windham College, an MD from Mount Sinai School of Medicine, an MPH in Health Policy and Management from Columbia University, and an MFA in Writing from Sarah Lawrence College. She is a past Associate Editor of *Lumina, Vol XIII*, the Sarah Lawrence College literary magazine. Her feature articles, essays, and profiles appear regularly in *The Palisades Newsletter 10964*. She is currently at work on a novel.

Robert Burke Warren is a writer and musician. He's ghost-written for Gregg Allman, and his liner notes appear on the award-winning CD *Live at Caffe Lena*. His work—musical and literary—is widely available via Google search, and in the Da Capo anthology *The Show I'll Never Forget*. His 2016 debut novel, *Perfectly Broken*, is easily obtainable. His songs appear on albums by Rosanne Cash and rockabilly queen Wanda Jackson, and The Roots used his tune "The Elephant in the Room" as John McCain's entrance theme on Late Night with Jimmy Fallon.

The Elusive Eagle: Charles McGill and the Anti-Trope

Joe Lewis

"Golf is a chronic and progressive illness. Once afflicted, all bets are off. You can
bet the farm on that!"
— Anonymous, circa 2016

Classically trained in the figurative painting tradition, a superb drafts-
person, colorist and writer with the gift of gab, Charles McGill is an
artist's artist. Formal preparation gave him entrée to the history of art
with extensive vascular connections to the High Renaissance, Dada,
Futurism, Modernism and ethnocentric contemporary practices. With
a well-stocked investigative toolkit, his ability to wield said implements
with aesthetic prowess is immediately evident when observing how he
handles relationships between materials, content, and form. Something
else becomes apparent as the viewer joins his trudge through difficult
subject matter. Regardless of the complexity or darkness of his revela-
tions, McGill never loses sight of beauty and craft—it's what makes his
work readily accessible on multiple levels simultaneously.

Ironically, though steeped within the fluid frame of race and
representation, his initial adoption of golfing paraphernalia as signifier
and manufactured agency had little to do with a quest for social
commentary's sweet spot. A devoted golfer himself, McGill's foray into
the sport's hierarchical world began in a serendipitous moment, when he
visited a gallery on his way to the links and someone said, "Do you mind if
I take a picture of you? I've never seen golf clubs in an art gallery before." [1]
McGill then realized the fertile possibilities of taking his love of the sport
into the studio.

Before that encounter, McGill made a few aerial views, oil stick
drawings of golf courses. They anchor his visual interest in the
game and especially its baggage as possible subject and pallet. These
early expressionist pictures, reminiscent of Kandinsky's elaborate
improvisational compositions, carve a semi-figurative way of looking at
the physical terrain. You can feel him dragging his percolating critical
discourse over the fairway, stripping it down to its most essential
elements while connecting his well-honed figurative training to an
exigent abstract urge that foreshadows his future dissection of the game
and its components.

---

1 *"Golf, Art and Dismantling Old Beliefs,"* BMCC News, *2016, Borough of Manhattan
Community College, CUNY, 10 December 2015 ‹http://www.bmcc.cuny.edu/news/news.
jsp?id=12663›.*

These abstractions would soon thrust through the "back nine to the frontline," and eventually usurp the didactic tropes of image/text, the figure, race, and commodification, embracing purity and immensity—the sweeping expanse of abstraction. It's difficult to fathom how one finds beauty through the lens of exclusion, but McGill gives both original and meaningful life in spite of their metaphysical opposition.

The 1999-2000 exhibition *Club Negro* is an excellent introduction to McGill's broad theoretical reach. Mercantilism sets the exhibit's tone. Dreadlocked balls and clubs, lynching images, and comparisons between lynching mobs and tournament viewing galleries provide the backdrop for McGill's confrontation of stereotypical, often unspoken thoughts that color and shape the dark recesses of the collective racist consciousness. Another seminal work from that period not included in this exhibition, *I am, I am not* (1999), consists of fifty-four single balls on tees that are tightly packed together in a rectangular case with the following handwritten declarations:

> *My name was never Uncle Tom.*
> *I have never been a runaway slave.*
> *I have never used a hot comb.*
> *I have never been an invisible man.*
> *I have never had a dream.*
> *I have never done anything by any means necessary.*

The message slices into the room like a serrated monolith. McGill's neo-conceptual quips are similar in depth and breadth to Jenny Holzer's *Truisms* (1977-present), her *Survival* series (1983-1985) in particular, with two caveats. Both question the underpinnings of contemporary life in oracular fashion, but Holzer scratches its back while McGill's machinations suck the marrow out of it. His are not political statements, but moral ones.

Club Negro's blunderbuss read on social class, privilege, place, and race created a praetorian plinth for McGill's first collaged bag. *Lynch Bag* (1999) explores the deeply flawed nature of master-race civilization by mining historic lynching images, past and present, and coupling their shared DNA of Black objectification by decoupaging on a vintage leather golf bag. The decoupage process is labor intensive. It's an amalgamation of cut images cemented together to form intricate designs and is thought to have originated in East Siberian tomb art, where Nomadic tribes decorated graves of their deceased with felt cutouts. As the practice expanded outward throughout the ancient world, it became more decorative and eventually a staple form of embellishment in both Asian and European royal courts. In its initial presentation, *Lynch Bag* was hung from the ceiling, like a floating tomb. For McGill, no symbiotic relationship is left to chance. And so, at that moment, he begins his long and tempestuous relationship with the golf bag.

The collage practice does not stray far from McGill's formal training as a figurative painter but, in fact, solidifies his interest in redefining the human form. The layering, working with identifiable images, building relationships and surfaces based on color, form, and rhythm is, as he has said, "painting without pigment." The golf bag, its potbelly and occasional protruding booty, especially when fully clubbed, has a structural similarity to a human figure in stasis. When used as an allusion, it brings him full circle back to his roots, underscoring the emotional realness of his musings.

Over the years, his *Baggage* series (1999-2010) has morphed in three stages: decorative surfacing, figurative conglomerations, and total reconstructions. His compositional formulas and critical extrapolations insert his practice into a long and storied tradition of artists who have borne the responsibility and weight of cultural illumination. Their perpetual repurposing chases the mutating American racial pathology. Though not as decorative, the political intensity of the illustrations in Sue Coe's *How to Commit Suicide in South Africa* (1984), that traces the history of apartheid, immediately comes to mind, as do Jacob Lawrence's very shadowy *War Series* (1946-1947), a series paintings that juxtapose composition, form, and perilous subtext.

McGill often returns to the figure. When he does, he takes no prisoners: it's in his blood. His aggregate bag compositions, *Night of Mischief* (2012), and *Fortress of Four* (2015), stand guard like hooded, blinged-out stele in front of some secret society's hideout or boundary markers establishing lines that shout, "once crossed, it's impossible to return." Bathed in the muted tones of a restricted palette, they channel the brute political anatomies of Philip Guston's use of KKK imagery. Similarly, another group of distant relatives is the anti-war activist Leon Golub's *White Squad* (1987), a series that codifies the arrest and interrogation of innocents by police or vigilante forces.

McGill's unapologetic figures stand tall. Their cut, twisted, torn and screwed surfaces charge into one's personal space with abandon and, like Civil War Night Riders, their disregard for humanity tries to redefine communities. Situated in the painful enclave of systemic inequality, they peer into the steaming cauldron of history repeating itself—silently chanting, casting spells, and marking their territories.

McGill's full body cast, *Arthur Negro II* (2007-2010), the multi-site performance, *Playing Through* (1998-2009), and the emergence of *The Former Black Militant Golf and Country Club* (1997) create a powerful nexus for McGill's maturing oeuvre, a culminating treatise. The argyle-clad, life-size portrait of the infamous Black Militant power broker and founder of "The Former Black Militant Golf and Country Club,"

Arthur Negro contemplates, with his heroic gaze, a future devoid of "the struggle," and plenty of prime "tee" time—somewhere off in the distance. But just in case, his beret is cocked to the side, an indication of being down and ready for a fight. And, he is well-armed.

McGill assumed this persona in the performance work *Playing Through*. On a few different occasions, he took to the streets of Harlem, Tribeca, and Hanoi. Peppering the gathering crowds with messages of revolution, he teaches putting techniques to passersby using the broad boulevards of 125th Street, MLK Blvd, and in some instances, vacant lots as fairways and greens. The performance cadence is unmistakably Black, and it's our first full on glimpse of McGill's acerbic humor as he reads from Malcolm X's speech, "After the Bombing," on a bullhorn, and then sets up his next shot, teeing off watermelons.

Much like Da Vinci's notebook drawings of the human body, McGill dissects the once segregated cultural, social, and commercial enterprise of golf. Unlike Da Vinci, instead of using his research to inform the creation of an ideal body, possibly in search of a Pygmalion event, the performance codex is his final nod to the figure, as we know it. From this point forward, his work is primarily abstract in nature but still saturated with subtle societal innuendos of control and submission, personified by McGill's savaging leather golf bags, crushing them, making them do things they don't want to do. Whereas the majority of his previous constructions and objects were assemblage based and read well from ground level, he now positions himself at 10,000 feet, turning his micro post-conceptual-structuralism (class, race, representation, control and subjugation) into the macro (purity and immensity).

The PGA was the last major sport to integrate. How's that for a construct? McGill's initial foray into abstraction, in some undefinable way, lifts the opaque veil of the post-racial illusion from the present. His abandoning of the figure was counter-intuitive, especially when considering his training. He just ran out of room for it, and the embedded academic historiography. He likens the struggle to release himself from the bonds of the Age of Enlightenment's darkest corners—a rationale for slavery, based on a hierarchy of races—like this, "it's like sneaking up on a wild boar in the woods and trying to skin it while it's still alive."[2] In a subtextual way, he begs the question—does the figure belong in 21st-century sculpture, when its origins represent the disintegration of reason?

It's becoming increasingly apparent, the twenty-first century is a time of the minority-majority preparing for a new dominant culture constructed by and for them. McGill's deeper incursions into abstraction, his skins, keep us tethered to an analog reality rather than fictive value systems distributed by the hegemonic capacity of capitalism.

---

2 *Ibid.*

Although some of his earliest non-representational pieces appear related to John Chamberlain's fused and twisted monumental shapes, they are not. On the contrary, aside from their instinctual fabrication, their intent could not be further from each other. Unlike Chamberlain's focus on cheap materials and junk sans political comment, and more akin to Melvin Edwards' *Lynching Fragments* (1960s-present), McGill's bailiwick reveals the severe fracture and dystopian agony of a society trying to survive while stretched and warped over a utopian iconographical reality. Indelibly shaped by notions of racial tension and segregation, they are removed performances, communing with the past, counting the moments while a self-defined cultural elite, trying everything it can to stay on top, implodes as a metaphor. ॐ

Reprinted courtesy of the author, Joe Lewis, and the Boca Raton Museum of Art.

Artist Statement

Charles McGill

"I find the golf bag to be a very political object due to its historical associations with class inequality and racial injustice. It resonates with me on increasingly deeper levels. It is both an object and subject that lends itself well to found object abstractions and assemblages that address these well-chronicled complexities.

Unlike modern golf bags, these vintage-style bags are constructed of very durable materials and heavy hardware that are extremely difficult to disassemble and manipulate. The tempered plastic, steel, heavy riveting and stitching, leather and vinyl resist structural change. The deconstruction process requires the use of several power tools, blades, drills and steel wire cutters. The often turbulent and frustrating process speaks to the larger predicament of dismantling the old socio-political mechanisms in favor of a new paradigm.

These old bags often have a thumbnail-sized tag with the words 'Made in the USA' and an American Flag embroidered onto a small tag sewn along a seam. Many of them were manufactured in the South, in particular, Jasper, Alabama; conceptually relevant to the work, this evocative detail of the Jim Crow-era serves as a very meaningful catalyst.

I try to expand the perceived boundaries of this material and the way in which discussions on race can be compelled and reconsidered. Race and representation are the conceptual DNA of my work, not a billboard for those issues."

ART: Charles McGill

Charles McGill, *Arthur Negro II*, 2007-10, Plaster, steel armature, acrylic paint, golf bag, collage, and other mixed media, 7.5' x 5' x 5', Photo credit: Pete Mauney, Courtesy of the Virginia Museum of Fine Art

Charles McGill, *Cadillac*, 2010, Collage on golf bag, 40" x 14" x 17",
Photo credit: Pete Mauney, Courtesy of the Virginia Museum of Fine Art

Charles McGill, *Lynch Bag*, 1999, Collage on golf bag, 38" x 14" x 17",
Photo credit: Pete Mauney, Courtesy of the artist and Pavel Zoubok Gallery

Charles McGill, *Target 51*, 2015, Golf bag parts on wood, 8' diameter,
Photo credit: Pete Mauney, Courtesy of the artist and Pavel Zoubok Gallery

Charles McGill, *Corset*, 2015, Reconfigured golf bags on wood armature, 60" x 14" x 14", Photo credit: Pete Mauney, Courtesy of the artist and Pavel Zoubok Gallery

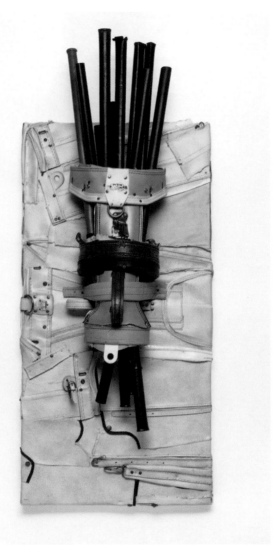

Charles McGill, *Sun Shaman*, 2013, Reconfigured golf bag parts on panel,
66" x 24" x 16", Photo credit: Pete Mauney,
Courtesy of the artist and Pavel Zoubok Gallery

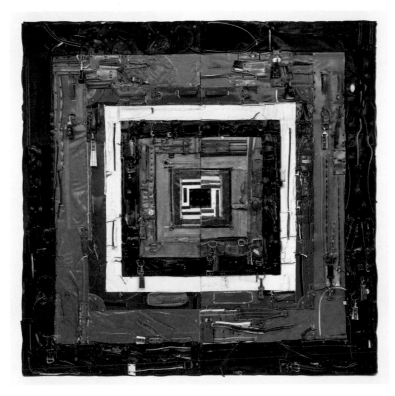

Charles McGill, *Dilemma*, 2016, Reconfigured golf bags on wood, 96" x 96" x 4",
Photo credit: Pete Mauney, Courtesy of the artist and Pavel Zoubok Gallery

Charles McGill, *Night of Mischief*, 2012, Reconfigured golf bag parts on panel,
48" x 48" x 15", Photo credit: Pete Mauney, Courtesy of the artist
and Pavel Zoubok Gallery

Charles McGill, *Blue Moon Tondo*, 2015, Golf bag parts on wood, 4' diameter,
Photo credit: Pete Mauney, Courtesy of the artist and Pavel Zoubok Gallery

Charles McGill, *Fortress For Four*, 2014-15, Reconfigured golf bags on wood
armature, 5.5' x 4.5' x 4.5', Photo credit: Pete Mauney,
Courtesy of the artist and Pavel Zoubok Gallery

Charles McGill, *Territories*, 2015, Reconfigured golf bag parts on wood panel,
4' diameter, Photo credit: Pete Mauney, Courtesy of the artist and
Pavel Zoubok Gallery

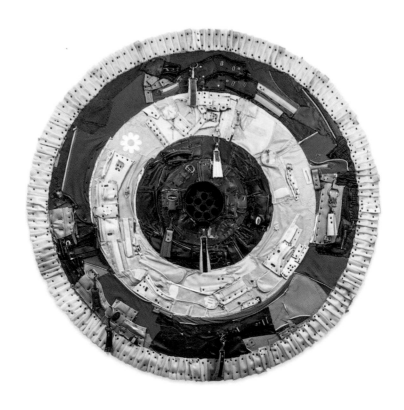

Charles McGill, *Summertime*, 2015, Golf bag parts on wood, 6' diameter,
Photo credit: Pete Mauney, Courtesy of the artist and Pavel Zoubok Gallery

Charles McGill, *White*, 2015, Golf bag parts on wood, 4' x 4',
Photo credit: Pete Mauney, Courtesy of the artist and Pavel Zoubok Gallery

Charles McGill, *Goat, Bull, Rooster, Horse*, 2014, Reconfigured golf bag parts, 23" x 20"x 11", Photo credit: Pete Mauney, Courtesy of the artist and Pavel Zoubok Gallery

Charles McGill, *Target (Tondo) 1964*, 2015, Reconfigured golf bag parts on wood panel, 4' diameter, Photo credit: Pete Mauney,
Courtesy of the artist and Pavel Zoubok Gallery

Charles McGill, *Broken Quilt*, 2016, Reconfigured golf bag parts on panel,
78" x 48" x 6", Photo credit: Pete Mauney, Courtesy of the artist
and Pavel Zoubok Gallery

Going Sailing

Jaclyn Van Lieu Vorenkamp

She's sitting astern, shirt buttoned up to her neck, cap visor pulled down low, shrinking to fit in the little bit of shade offered by the strip of canvas roofing. It is very hot and there's not much of a breeze. She and her husband are motoring out of the channel into the sound. The chugging of the engine and the cloud of diesel exhaust travel with them, they are moving so slowly.

There's traffic in the harbor, in all directions. Sunfish dart among the larger vessels, their sailors blinded by their sails, headed straight toward her and her husband, then at the last possible second, they come about and skim away as if it were nothing. She imagines dark blood spreading along the subsurface currents around the boat and a smashed head bobbing like a marker in the dirty water. What would it be like to accidentally kill someone? Maybe painless, without consequence, like a dream, just offer a simple Oh excuse me! and continue on. She's glad the Sunfish has escaped, although she could have found some release in feeling the impact, hearing the screams, and having this going-out-for-a-sail business aborted by the crisis and the consequent need to return to land.

He's on the forward deck, busy bringing in the lines and fenders. He misses the scene. She calls out to him, "What shall we do about these Sunfish?" He straightens up and watches another tiny craft hurtling toward them, just yards away, the sailor blinded by the sail, like a huge umbrella thrust against the wind. He says nothing. She veers the boat to the right but now they're in danger of grounding outside the channel and she asks again for direction. He is supposedly the expert, after all. She feels a kind of reckless resignation to his doubtful skill, a willful handing over of her life. She has to be willing to die so they can go sailing together this afternoon. Why does she do it? Out of love? Is it out of love that he asks her to? The Sunfish comes about and skips off.

"It's peaceful out here," he says.

She looks at his face for signs that he's kidding. He looks back expectantly.

"Perhaps when we get under way, it'll feel peaceful," she says.

He appears disappointed, even suspicious that she's being deliberately uncooperative. It's generally understood that few things are more beautiful or more calming than the sight of a sailboat out on the water catching the light and the wind.

He's not wearing his life vest. What if he fell overboard? She wouldn't know what to do. She feels he's being irresponsible by not instructing her on the use of the life saving contraption that's hanging on the railing, or what to do with the boat if he isn't there to tell her, how to find him in the waves, pull him out of the water. It's very hard to see someone bobbing in the water. What if he's unconscious and can't put the life saving thing on even if she were able to throw it exactly to him? She reads on the cover of the device that you should not tow a person who's wearing it because you could drown him.

"What do I do in case you fall overboard?" she asks.

"Come get me," he smiles.

"Yes, but how?"

"Simple. Turn on the engine, drop the sails, unfold the ladder here, and throw me this thing."

"But it says here you shouldn't lower the ladder if the engine's on."

"Then turn it off," he says.

It occurs to her that she doesn't know how to turn off the engine, which lines go to which sails, what the life saving thing looks like, or how heavy it is. She asks. He is patient. Obviously, he will not be falling overboard and all this worrying is threatening to spoil his afternoon.

"If you're unconscious and I can't pull you in, this says I should leave you . . ."

"Yes, just leave me." He laughs.

"No, not *leave* you. Good grief! Leave you tethered to the side of the boat and call for help."

"Okay," he says.

She thinks he doesn't know what to do. He has a general concept, but he doesn't really know. What if she were the one to fall overboard, not that she has any plans to move from her spot in the shade. She would probably be drawn by the current into the propeller blades and her hands and part of her face would be sliced off, possibly her whole head and she would hemorrhage to death in the water while he was dropping the sails and turning on or off the engine and lowering the ladder and throwing her the life saving device that without hands now she won't be able to grab. Bobbing in the water, face down, if it were still attached, her arms outstretched at her sides in an expanding pool of blood. Would she appear tragic, like Elaine of Astolat, dying of love on the bottom of her skiff?

They're passing the channel towers embellished with the nests of herons and terns. Cormorants stand in rows along the jetties, spreading their wings to dry in the sun. Others swim alongside, their water-logged bodies sinking, their heads and necks just above the water line.

He scrambles aft and unties the mainsail. Then he scrambles back to the stern to release the lines. Her job is to keep the boat motoring straight into the wind, to keep from running into things, like the old lighthouse, submerged rocks, lobster pots, other boats. Sometimes she has to swerve to miss something and the sail takes wind while he's hoisting it, and yanks the boom into his chest. If the boom struck him with sufficient force, it could knock him overboard, and then she would have to drop the sails, turn on the engine—wait! the engine's already on! turn it off!—throw him the life preserver, and lower the ladder and hope he hadn't been struck unconscious or killed.

Should he die before she does, she gets their entire estate, apart from his family heirlooms, which she is to distribute to his children at the time of his death. There are just a few things: a family bible bound in leather, a silver loving cup, the ring with the family crest. His older son is in line for these ancient artifacts because the family still observes the rights and rituals of primogeniture, at least in this matter, but he's indifferent to them. The younger son is more interested. She's not sure how to handle this. And then there are the other things his boys will want: the prints, the books, the photography equipment, everything in his studio.

Actually, the studio would make a very nice little rental apartment if she can figure out where to put a kitchen, or it could make an excellent writing space for herself. She would want to upgrade the cabinetry and add bookcases—there's room for more bookcases on all the walls—and add some comfortable chairs and a daybed for reading and dreaming. And she would get rid of that cold slate gray he painted the walls, brighten the place up a bit, give it some warmth.

She's watched people die before, in the hospital; she's even pushed one or two over the edge, as an act of mercy, but only people who really needed it, people who had outlived their lives. Perhaps there was only one, only one she remembers, anyway, and he knew what she was doing. It was easy—she just gave him a little more morphine than usual. It was their secret, her parting gift to him. You won't feel this, she told him, and he didn't.

Out on the sound, the sails fill with wind and the boat scuds along the surface of the water in tandem with the clouds scudding across the sky. She ponders the word "scud." A good word but easily overused. Even once may be too much. But what else are they and the clouds doing? In the distance, the underbellies of the clouds darken and a gray haze begins to blur the shoreline. The winds are gusting over ten knots. They're miles from shore and in water over a hundred feet deep. The boat leans into the water, racing along its rim, the sail threatening to dip into the waves and capsize them. She wonders if the keel can snap off; she's heard of such things happening. She holds on to the railing with both hands as sprays of water dampen her hair and her clothing. She braces her feet against the bench opposite her.

"Isn't this magnificent?" he says, looking at her in a kind of rapture. He holds the lines in his hand, like the reins of a powerful steed.

"Yes," she says. "Elemental."

What if her husband died some other way? What if he just collapsed? Once, he had chest pains in his office and she met him in the Emergency Room. The nurses put him on a stretcher, took off his clothes, gave him oxygen, put in an IV, ran an EKG, and when he said the pressure was worsening, they slipped a tablet of nitroglycerin under his tongue. Within seconds, the pain receded. This meant it came from his heart. She stepped behind the head of his stretcher so he couldn't see her eyes well with tears.

If he dies before she does, the first thing she'll do is sell the boat. Probably no one will buy it. Used boats are very difficult to get rid of. She will need to hire someone to sand off the serial numbers and sink it in some marsh somewhere.

The cloud cover has grown denser, blocking the sun. The wind rises. Rain drops pock the water's surface and pelt them in the face. A rumbling sound rolls toward them from out near the horizon.

She asks if it's time to go back.

The wind is coming at them directly from the harbor so they tack back and forth across the sound, gaining speed, cutting through the swells. The water looks cold and thick, heavy as syrup. She would not be able to push it off her if she fell in. Her shoes would fill with water and drag her to the bottom. No one would find her so deep down and the currents would drag her away, but she could leave a trail in the sandy bottom with her heavy feet, in case rescuers came to look for her. Her hair floating about her face like seaweed, fingerlings nibbling at her skin, bits of bloodless flesh suspended in the murk, her arms floating, tangling in the lines of lobster pots, the lobsters trapped in their pots gazing at her with envy, or is it hunger, as she drags a trail with her feet in the sandy bottom.

If she dies first, her husband gets the entire estate, except for her family heirlooms, which he is to give to her son at the time of her death. She believes he will fulfill this obligation faithfully and with generosity. He is a good man, but still it seems unfair that she should drown so young, with the best part of her life ahead of her. She imagines him keening inconsolably over her remains, and then when he recovers, selling the house and her gardens in which she toiled so lovingly and obsessively, and moving to the city where his heart has always been.

The weather eases. He navigates the boat toward the mouth of the harbor. It's time to start up the engine and drop the sail. He hands her the tiller, telling her to stay into the wind while he scrabbles up on deck to flake the mainsail. They pass the old lighthouse, the towers marking the mouth of the channel, the cormorants drying their wings. There are few boats in the channel at this time of day; they are among the last to come in. She keeps a sharp eye on the buoys, "red right return," she repeats silently over and over. As they slow to a chug, he takes back the tiller and gracefully maneuvers the boat through the crowded marina and into its slip, jumps lightly onto the dock and with a swift, deft motion, wraps the tie securely around a cleat.

She clambers out of the boat onto the rocking dock. Now it is just a matter of walking straight ahead to land. ❧

CALAMITY AND OTHER STORIES

Nicole Haroutunian

Calamity and Other Stories by Daphne Kalotay is a book I came to at random, on the shelves of my hometown library about a decade ago. I must have run through my stash of holiday reading too quickly and needed a supplement. Drawn to it because of the lopsided cupcake on the cover, I was taken in by ten-year-old friends Rhea and Callie in the first story, "Serenade," and the specificity of the startling moment Rhea witnesses between their mothers.

The story "Anniversary" comes at the book's midpoint. It is full of funny, telling passages like this one, where the protagonist, Eileen, describes her future daughter-in-law, the now-adult Callie:

> Her crotch is always showing. She always wears short skirts, and I swear every time I look there's this *view."* Eileen shakes her head at herself, because even though it's true it's not at all what she means.

I loved the conspiratorial satisfaction I got reading this—of course, I knew what Eileen was trying to say, already having gotten to know Callie through Rhea's eyes. As Eileen prepares for her son's upcoming wedding, she reflects her relationship with his father, whom she met at a kibbutz.

I'm not precious about marriage, but this story comes as close as I've ever seen to evoking its allure. For a while, every time I was invited to a wedding—even when I got married myself—I tried to find a section to letterpress print as a gift or to read aloud during the ceremony. But there is no perfect quote to pull; the meaning of the story is too active, woven through every sentence and choice. Like the best short stories, "Anniversary" is irreducible.

Its irreducibility hasn't stopped me from dismantling and analyzing it, though. At the end of "Anniversary," Eileen is lying in bed with her hands clasped, a gesture that has accrued so much meaning by that time that even now, despite having read the story nearly to the point of memorization, I have to hold my own hands over my stomach thinking about it, the feeling that twists there is so intense. What really compounds the emotion is that, a few paragraphs earlier, Kalotay lets slip a small secret the book had been keeping, a revelation that alters not only the story but the collection as a whole. Unlike the accumulating details about Callie, which deepen and enrich the book, this moment truly transforms it. I think I can say without ruining the experience for those who haven't read it yet that Kalotay accomplishes this with only one word: honeymoon. "Anniversary" functions as a world unto itself, but also a lens for the collection as a whole, sharpening and bringing into focus what came before and distorting what is still to come.

When I first read *Calamity*, I hadn't started to write a collection of linked stories yet. But that effect, the way that one word—*honeymoon*—cast back over the stories I'd already read, changing them in retrospect, became something I chased. I wrote a linked collection filled with details like an early conversation misremembered a hundred pages later, a song played in one story and heard in another, a character's recurring ache whose origin—a dramatic fall during an escape from a locked bar—is shown only in the manuscript's last pages. After working on it for years, I sent it to a contest and discovered, as it disappeared into the mailbox, that what I'd been feeling in my stomach when I reread it one last time before printing it was not that clasped hands, honeymoon feeling, but disappointment. I'd made the book too neat and tried too hard; I'd written the honeymoon right out of it. I hoped it would lose the contest and it did.

Soon after I first read *Calamity*, an email arrived in my inbox from my college's alumni association, announcing an event with Daphne Kalotay, class of '92. I hadn't known we had this connection. At the bookstore, Kalotay read the story "Serenade." I bought a copy of the book and, as she signed it for me, I told her that while I thought "Serenade" was beautiful, I really loved "Anniversary." She paused, pen in hand, and looked up at me. "That story is my favorite, too," she said, adding something like, "But it's so quiet. I'm not supposed to read it out anymore."

Last year, I finally published a collection of linked short stories. That spring, I read from it at my hometown library. The audience was populated by my immediate family members, a handful of old friends, a few of their mothers and one high school freshman, an aspiring writer, who came up to me after and, clutching a book from the small stash I brought to sell, asked, "Did you *really* grow up here?"

Recently, I discovered that, despite organizing that reading for me, the library does not stock my book. I just did a search and it turns out they don't have *Calamity* on the shelves, either. I may not remember correctly where I came across my first copy of *Calamity*, but I hope that teenager remembers where she got her copy of *Speed Dreaming*. It was in Montvale, New Jersey, a place where writers really can grow up. ❧

Water, Water Everywhere

Matt Jones

Shari Stone owned about thirty acres of mountain laurel and dust in the northwest hills of Lago Vista. She was my boss, and I worked fifty hours a week as her personal assistant; occasionally, she paid me extra to make the long and winding drive from South Austin up to her place so I could clear brush or haul away furniture that she deemed not to fit the aesthetic of her redesign.

Recently, she offered me a burnished blue leather armchair that she'd purchased from West Elm. When I told her there was no way it was going to fit into my hatchback, she offered to hire some movers and a truck to take care of it. When I told her that my apartment wasn't big enough, she said I should consider moving further out of the city where I could get more square footage per dollar.

"Or," Leanne had said in a tone closer to acid than breath, "she could just give you a fucking raise so we don't have to move even further away from your actual office." We were on Red Bud Isle, a peninsula-shaped dog park that extended like a finger between the two banks of Lake Austin. Leanne's dog Runt nosed the heaving fish trapped in the ever-evaporating puddles of mud. "Or," she said, her voice rising to epiphanic levels, "she could stop thinking of inane reasons to call you over to her house whenever she wants."

Leanne and I shared a two bedroom, so technically, our apartment was big enough to fit the armchair, but I declined the offer because gifts from Shari tended to get Leanne worked up, which, in turn, made me uneasy because I felt this constant tension between my girlfriend and my boss. And there was the fact that I thought it might actually do us some good to move further from downtown, to get a bigger place. I liked the blue armchair. I said, "Think about it this way. If we moved, we could have a yard. Then we wouldn't always have to drive to the dog park."

Leanne rolled her eyes and I watched Runt try and tunnel into the cracked mud where the water had receded. "I better not find out that you've been looking at places behind my back with some realtor. And," she added, incensed, "you like the dog park."

It was so hot out that the buttons on my shirt burned small pink circles in a vertical line up my stomach and chest. I saw that Runt had something in his mouth and was squeezing his way through a thicket of Sugarberry so he could gnaw in private at whatever it was. I said, "I don't love this one. Why can't we go to Zilker?"

Leanne clapped for Runt and said, "Because I don't want to have to keep him on a leash. He won't stop pulling."

Runt came trotting over with burrs hanging ornamental from his fur. His body smelled like fish and microbes and he stood up and pushed a set of muddy paws into Leanne's leg. "But this is the kind of shit that happens when he's not leashed. He makes a mess everywhere."

Leanne inhaled deeply and narrowed her eyes at me. "I swear to God right now. If this is about the couch," but all she could muster was holding a rigid finger in front of my face. There was so much frustration bound up in that one fingertip that I felt that, if she were to touch me with it, I might just go flying backward.

The couch, which was really a tan chesterfield sofa, was the first thing Shari had ever given me. She said it was "too lean" for her place. And at first, Leanne loved it, so much in fact that it became the centerpiece of our apartment. Dirty clothes were draped over the back of it. Drunk friends melted into it. Runt hid his rawhides in between the leather cushions. The very day I even suggested that we might try and keep it clean, Leanne said, "What do you care? It's not like we paid for it." And though my response had only sent us spiraling into the same argument over and over before, I found myself repeating my same words at the dog park.

"I know that we didn't pay for it, but it was a gift, okay? I don't think I'm asking a lot when I say we need to take better care of it."

Leanne knelt and rubbed Runt between the ears. I thought I saw a circus of bugs springing forth from his coat. "You know what," she said. "It's not even the gifts that bother me. If she wants to force bathmats and drapes on us, then fine. What really bothers me is how fucking flattered you are by them. But know this, Jacob," and she stood up to meet my gaze. "Shari is as old as your mother, okay? Just think about that."

Leanne had theories about why Shari gave us things, theories that didn't exist before the extended workdays and calls after eight and Saturday hours. We had a Pottery Barn lamp that looked like a golden rabbit in our entryway and Leanne acted as if every time I turned it on or off, there was some metaphysical alarm that got tripped halfway across town in Shari's mini-mansion.

I let out a long sigh and said, "She's just trying to help us out."

"Can you stop saying that?" Leanne snapped, slipping Runt's leash onto his collar.

"Stop saying what?" I asked.

"Us," Leanne moaned. "You act as if she's giving this stuff to us, when really it's all for you. She's doing it to get under my skin."

"That's insane," I said.

Leanne's eyes bulged. "Oh no. You don't get to call me crazy. She's trying to smoke me out. Hell, she's got the money. She'll just keep redesigning her house and calling you over on the weekends and trying to push fucking rugs and stainless steel cookware on you until our apartment is so full that I'm out on the street. Well, let me tell you something: that is not going to happen. You'll quit your job before that happens."

"I'm not going to quit my job," I told her. After graduation, it had taken me the better part of a year to find something that wasn't part time. The market had been terrible and though Shari had her quirks, she was successful. The law firm was her own. The house in Lago Vista was her own. She kept horses on a ranch just outside of Dripping Springs. I had a mildly impressive degree in Business, a heap of student debt, and Shari said, "You've also got a lot of potential. I can tell. I'm never wrong."

We climbed into Leanne's car, mostly because I refused to take mine to the dog park anymore, and Runt leapt into the back and curled into a wet half-moon in a patch of sunlight. The ignition faltered and then caught. We cranked the windows down because air conditioning meant more gas and we were both soaked through with sweat already anyway. Even still, the air that slapped us in the face felt feverish. The whole interior smelled like Runt and I said, "So you'll wash him before we go inside?"

"I need to do it in the bathtub."

"What? Why?"

She turned onto the Congress Bridge and I looked out at Lake Austin, so low in some spots that I could see straight through to the bottom. "Because, Jacob," she explained. "Last time I used the hose, one of our narc neighbors reported me for water waste and we got fined fifty dollars."

I leaned my head out of the window and sucked down a mouthful of heat. One of the ways to effectively end a conversation between us was to bring up money. Much like the fish stranded in small, standing puddles of water, scales being dehydrated one by one, Leanne and I were in a rough patch. We fought over bills sometimes. She wanted to go on vacation, to recharge, but we were always low on money. Plus, Leanne had another theory that said Shari would never give me the time off anyway.

There was a part of me that wanted to immediately get home and hop in the shower and rinse all of the grime of the day off my body, but there was also an equally insistent part that knew I'd need to let Runt get bathed first. Because if it didn't happen right away, then it wouldn't happen at all.

Come early August, it hadn't rained for 71 days, which wasn't all that uncommon for the Hill Country. What was interesting about the last two months was that every day had achieved a temperature of over one hundred degrees. There was a burn ban from Houston to Midland. APD officers were stationed every couple of miles throughout the green belt to make sure people weren't smoking on the biking trails and there were signs posted all around town urging residents to call and snitch on any neighbors that employed the use of automatic sprinkler systems. But Shari didn't have neighbors.

Her house was clouded by acacia tree and live oak and when I was finished hosing down the mountain laurels, I was then supposed to go and wet the front yard to keep the dust from rising up and coating the floor-to-ceiling windows that made up most of the house.

Despite the heat, it was a beautiful piece of land. I could easily see owning something similar in the future once I saved up enough. While Shari didn't pay me a king's ransom, there were perks. Lunches at the steakhouse on the corner of 5th and Congress. Cocktails with investors. Shari even ran an incubator alongside the firm. Once a year, she'd hear pitches for business ideas from young entrepreneurs and one lucky person would walk away with the Stone Prize for Innovation and Excellence, which, while also not directly consisting of money, did offer a year's worth of free legal services, office space, and branding advice.

After I was finished with the yard, it was half past ten and I walked inside to find Shari considering two different but oddly similar paintings on her couch. She didn't turn around and said, "Quick, which one?"

Because she valued decisiveness, I said, "The one on the left."

She nodded slowly as if having some sort of internal debate and said, "Excellent. You can have the other. I don't want to clutter the walls."

Then she turned around and smiled. She was tall and lean with fine lines etched around her eyes. "Are you all finished?" she asked.

I nodded and said, "That should be everything," instead simply choosing to not acknowledge her suggestion about the painting.

She pursed her lips and said, "I almost forgot. The shower is finally finished. I never thought it would get done, but it really is."

She was referring to an outdoor shower tucked into a corner of the deck that wrapped around the house. Shari was a neat freak and I sometimes suspected that she'd had it installed only so I wouldn't track dirt inside.

"That's great," I told her. "How's it look?"

She tipped her head to one of the sliding glass doors and said, "Come see. You can tell me whether or not I got ripped off by that contractor." And while I didn't know anything about construction or architecture, it was nice to know that she sometimes consulted me on things. What to order. What to drink. How to file something. And sure, she often asked for the advice after the decision was already made, but it felt good nonetheless.

I followed her out onto the porch and gazed at a gleaming, steel showerhead mounted into one wall of the house. The shower stall itself was only walled in on two sides. Other than that, blue jays, armadillos, and roaming deer alike were free to have a peek.

"So," she said, "what do you think?"

"It's excellent," I told her. "I wish I had one."

She tipped her head to the side as if having a tiny revelation. "Well you can be the first to break it in!"

I swallowed and looked at my watch. I told Leanne I wouldn't be home any later than noon. I said, "That's okay. I don't want to mess it up."

"Oh, please," Shari insisted. "I feel bad for sending you back home all sweaty and gross. I'm sure Leanne must detest me."

They had met before, Leanne and Shari. Once. In between receiving an end table and a Vita-mixer. Shari invited us both out to her place for dinner and we ate on the back part of the porch and drank wine that was colored pink and orange by the sunset that eclipsed the glasses. I thought we'd had a perfectly nice time, but as soon as we got into the car and backed out of the driveway, Leanne confessed, "Wow. That was painful."

I checked my rearview mirror as we drove away and was momentarily blinded by a searing purple in the sky. "I thought it was nice," I said. "What did you think about that . . . that . . . what was it? Braised scaloppini?"

Leanne snorted. "Look at you, the little gourmand." She held her arm out in front of the dashboard, swirled the contents of an invisible wine glass, and said, "I'm detecting hints of Sage. Lavender. Chocolate and," she sniffed like a rat above the unseen rim, "pretentious bullshit."

I turned the wheel and pulled out onto the main road and Leanne said, "No offense, but your boss is kind of a snob."

"For inviting us to dinner?" I asked.

Leanne rolled her eyes and said, "For trying to make me feel stupid for not knowing which fork to use for the first course. And Jesus, did you hear what she said about my dress? 'I've always loved how casual this city is,'" Leanne echoed in a high and whiny pitch.

"Austin is casual," I told her. "And she doesn't even talk like that."

"As if you even noticed," Leanne said. "She was practically fawning all over you."

"That's just Shari," I told her. "She wants to impress people. You should take it as a compliment."

Which, in a way, was how I thought about the situation when she insisted I try the outdoor shower: She was trying to be kind by not having to send me home covered in dirt to my girlfriend who was waiting for me to get back so we could talk about whether or not I'd asked her about the thing I was supposed to ask her about. And because I still hadn't asked her the thing I was supposed to ask her about, and because Leanne would kill me if I didn't ask, I said, "Sure, but I don't really have clothes or anything."

Shari held up a hand and said, "You don't worry about it. I've got everything you need." With that, she pulled the lever and a stream of thick water poured from the head. It splashed her arm and she said,

"Perfect temperature. You just do what you do and I'll make sure to get you a towel."

After she was gone, I glanced around to make sure nobody was there. But of course, no neighbors. Had there been any, they surely would have rung up the secret H2O police and sent them my way.

I tossed my clothes over the railing that ran around the porch and stepped under the stream. The water was cold, but because of the heat in the air, it did feel just right. I wet my hair and watched rivulets of muck make their way down my chest and stomach and legs until they disappeared between the seams of the wood.

And it was only once I was starting to get clean that I realized Leanne might be more upset at the fact that I'd taken a shower at my boss's house. However, I also hoped that once I asked about the thing I was supposed to ask about and had been given a solid yes, it wouldn't really matter.

"How's it feel?" a voice called through the partial wall that separated the water from the window.

I called back, "It's great."

Shari said, "I just realized I forgot to give you soap."

"That's okay," I told her. "I'll just rinse."

"Don't be silly," she said, and I heard her voice growing louder in my ears until she appeared standing in front of me.

I immediately dropped a hand beneath my waist and she hiccupped laughter and said, "Oh I've seen it all before."

She set down three bottles in front of me and said, "Now the dark green one is shampoo and the light green is body wash. I'm not sure if you condition, but I'll leave this one here for you too." Then she faced out toward the open acreage and said, "Boy we could really use some rain. If it stays this dry, I just might have to get you to dig a moat around the house."

Then she turned sharply toward me. "That's just what I'm talking about," and she sighed and I was pretty sure that what she was talking about was the water pouring down from the showerhead, except in exponentially amplified quantities all across the county. She stuck a hand under the stream and sighed again. "Refreshing."

I saw that as perhaps my best moment to ask her the thing I was supposed to ask about. Leanne had another theory that every gift Shari gave us was a power move. Something she did so she could demonstrate that she had the upper hand. That she had the better life. That she was in charge. I said, "Umm, Shari."

She raised her eyebrows to show she was listening and I said, "Leanne and I were wanting to get out of town for a few days next week. Just to unwind. And I just wanted to see if it might be okay to be out of the office. Maybe take a long weekend."

Her eyebrows stayed frozen in place and she inhaled deeply. "Well, where does Leanne want to go? Because I can give hotel recommendations. I could even put the two of you up."

It was a nice offer, but I knew Leanne would hate it. "Oh, we couldn't," I told her. "That would be too much."

Shari narrowed her eyes and said, "Well, sure. You two deserve to take some time off. Hell, it seems that you probably don't get to spend any time together as is." Then she glanced into the stream of water and said, "You should probably turn that off now. Don't want to waste too much."

We left for New Braunfels on a Thursday morning where I had booked a small cottage on the Guadalupe. We had suffered brief visions of a getaway in Denver or DC, but planes tickets were expensive. Then there was a spontaneous spark of desire that led us to picturing a sultry, alcohol-soaked weekend on Bourbon Street in New Orleans, but Texas had recently declared a state of emergency and closed the I-10 going east because of the fires that were burning up the highway around Sealy. And, of course, there was the matter of Runt, who couldn't simply be left at home. Who couldn't be boarded. So why not bring him?

New Braunfels was only about an hour from Austin, but being that we only ever spent time at our apartment or at work, it felt long enough to seem like we had escaped something. Before we had left, Leanne insisted that I didn't tell Shari we were going to New Braunfels. "If that woman knows we're only an hour away, then she'll never let us have any peace."

But at lunch on Wednesday, Shari weaseled it out of me. She said, "It's not like you to keep secrets. I thought we shared things."

Shari's first call came in around Buda and my phone buzzed in the cup holder while Leanne said, "Your mother's calling. Do you want me to get it?"

She called again around San Marcos and once more passing through Hunter, and despite the lingering voicemails, my phone stopped buzzing by the time we arrived.

The cottage itself was a quaint pale yellow with a tin roof and blue window sidings. Shari might have called it rustic, but Shari wasn't there. It was just me and Leanne and Runt and the dark green Guadalupe lined by bald cypress and water moccasins that nested within the leaves. Was it not for the burn ban sign nailed directly into the trunk of the live oak that overhung half the tin roof, you'd think we were in a different world altogether.

We had barely so much as set our bags inside the door before Leanne started peeling her clothes free from her body and digging around for her swimsuit. Runt disappeared down the hall and I said, "Don't let him pee in here. We'll lose the deposit."

Her bikini strings hanging loose down her back, Leanne huffed and called for Runt. When he came, she ushered him outside and asked, "Are there tubes here?"

I nodded. "The website said so. They should be in one of the closets. We'll just have to blow them up."

Leanne stalked off down the hall and a few moments later I heard her exhaling as hard as she could into the tiny plastic nozzles. Then she called, "Can you do it? I'm not having any luck."

It was around two in the afternoon and I took over tube duty while Leanne slathered herself in sunscreen. My cheeks felt like they were about to pop trying to force air through the dense, rubber walls of each tube and I could hear Runt barking outside. I felt Leanne grab at the bottom of my shirt and shimmy it up over my shoulders. She pressed slick palms into my back and rubbed the lotion in small circles. "Don't want you to burn," she said.

When I was finished, I changed into my suit and grabbed the tubes. Leanne fished a bottle of whiskey out of our luggage and we crunched our way over dead grass to the river's edge. The water looked low and slow and Runt was yammering away at a twist of cypress roots that dangled like dozens of pairs of legs inside the water.

Leanne uncapped the whiskey and held it up between us. "What do you say?" she asked. "To us?"

She tipped the bottle back and chugged longer than I could count and passed it to me. "To us," I said.

She hooted up into the sky, tossed her bikini top to the side, and charged for the water. Runt went splashing in after her, and for a moment, I wondered if this experience might make her reconsider moving further out from the city. On the other side of the river were only dense tangles of root and dried bark. The whole place felt like a garden all our own. I imagined Shari surveying the property and the cottage and saying, "It's quaint. I don't know how I feel about the singing fish above the fireplace, but it has potential."

Leanne floated on her back in a meager patch of shade and I slipped my suit down to my ankles, ready to join her when I heard Runt start yelping. I couldn't see him at first, but I saw a long, black sliver of muscle slithering over the water's surface. It passed right by Leanne and kept on going downstream, then Runt came paddling pathetically out of the cypress roots.

Leanne was still on her back, the water in her ears having kept her from noticing what was happening and I thought as to how nice that must be: to be completely unaware of reality.

I yanked up my trunks and dashed forward to where Runt was limping on the shore and I yelled, "Leanne!"

Startled, she dropped beneath the surface and soaked her hair before popping back up, the water at her belly button. "What?" she said, startled. "What is it?"

I picked up Runt in my arms, which, given that it was such a rare occurrence, was probably enough to tell Leanne something was wrong. When she got out of the water, she ran over and I said, "I think a snake bit him. I heard him whimpering and saw one swim right down the river."

Her eyes widened and she took Runt from my arms. He was whimpering and shaking and she said, "What the fuck? When?"

I said, "Just now. We should get him to a vet."

She seemed shocked, almost unsure of what I was saying, but then something registered on her face and she jolted straight to the car and yanked the passenger side door hard. "It's locked, Jacob. The car is locked."

I ran inside to get my keys and tossed them to her. Then I dashed back toward the banks and she screamed, "Jacob, what the fuck are you doing? Get in the car!"

The window was open and Runt must have been quivering on her lap because I couldn't see him. Instead, all I could see was Leanne's bare chest, a glassy bewilderment in her eyes. I grabbed her top from the grass and held it up in the air.

When I climbed behind the wheel, I tossed it on her lap and said, "You can't just go out into the world topless."

She fumbled to put it on and said, "Don't fucking lecture me right now. Just drive." I supposed that the turn of events, if anything, were more likely to reinforce Leanne's love of the city. Where she was close to bars and coffee shops and her friends. Where she could go out late and stay out later and stumble back home to the comfort of the tan chesterfield sofa. Sometimes, just before she passed out, she liked to rub the leather over and over in small circles and say, "So cool on my skin. So cool."

After a long night in the emergency clinic, I had another voicemail. I'd already managed to covertly listen to the first three when I had to shuttle between the vet and the cottage to get Leanne something to wear.

"Hi, Jake," Shari started. "I forgot to tell you that I had a bunch of road food—chips and jerky and what not—leftover from when my nephew came to visit. That little brat hardly touched it. My sister's got him doing this whole vegan thing. Anyway, doesn't Leanne like that kind of stuff? Let me know if she wants it. I'll have it in a box on the front porch."

Delete.

"Hey, me again. Don't forget that we have an early meeting on Monday morning. Breakfast at Annie's. Might be good to talk strategy/ wardrobe beforehand. Let me know if you have a few free minutes while you're away."

Delete.

"I was trying to work the remote access to the office computer and I couldn't remember the number for the IT guy. Did we switch? Call me when you can. I hurt my back the other day trying to remove some of the tools you were using and I can't drive into the office."

Delete.

Delete.

I assumed the one I'd left unheard was only Shari telling me that she knew somebody who owned or cooked for a restaurant that overlooked the river. That she could get us reservations or comped meals. Shari had good taste. It was one of the things I liked about our business outings. She wasn't opposed to having a few glasses of good wine and extending a late lunch into early cocktails. I used to be worried about drinking in front of her. I didn't want to come off as unprofessional, but she said, "There's nothing unprofessional about taking a little pleasure in what you do. In the same way I wouldn't begrudge a kindergarten teacher for stepping into the bathroom for a joint during naptime, I wouldn't hold it against a lawyer for settling into a glass of pinot over lunch. Is that right?" she asked. "Kindergarten teacher?"

Caught off guard, I said, "Who?"

Shari said, "Leanne."

"No, preschool," I clarified.

Shari picked up the stem of her glass and stared intently at the liquid inside of it. "I'm sure she's exhausted working around all those kids. Just imagine if she did it full time. Have you two talked about that? Kids?" But before I could answer, Shari tipped her head back and laughed. "Who am I kidding? You're both too young to be thinking about that. You've got long lives and lots of twists and turns ahead of you," and to that, she raised her glass.

I supposed the snakebite was one of those twists and turns. When I got back to the vet, Leanne sat crumpled in a waiting room chair. She looked at me sleepy-eyed and said, "I'm starving."

I sat next to her and said, "How's he doing?"

She stretched her arms out and said, "Better. But weak. Can you run out and get us something?"

"Food?" I asked.

She nodded and said, "Maybe burgers if you can find a place."

I sighed. I didn't want to fight. We were both exhausted, but I worried about the extent of the vet bill. The anti-venom. The intravenous fluids. In the panic of the day before, I'd offered to call Shari and ask her to help us out, but Leanne ended up putting in a desperate call to her parents and maxing out one of her own credit cards. "I don't want her help, Jacob. He's not her dog," she shrieked, implying that Shari's assistance might then somehow cede her some majority share of Runt's ailing body, and an ever further stake in our relationship.

I thought longingly about the box of snack food that Shari had left on her porch for us. I said, "Burgers, huh?"

"Jacob," she pleaded, sounding on the verge of tears.

Then my phone buzzed in my pocket. I saw it was Shari calling and Leanne said, "Don't. Not now."

I swallowed and sent the call to voicemail and Leanne seemed to relax. Then there was another and another, and by the fourth one, I picked up. I saw Leanne's face flare right about the time Shari said, "Jacob! I've been trying to reach you. We're being evacuated over here and I need help getting my things into the car."

"What?" I said. "What do you mean you're being evacuated?"

That got Leanne's attention and she stood up and mouthed, *What does she want?*

I covered up the receiver and said, "Lago Vista is being evacuated. She needs help getting her stuff out of there."

Leanne furrowed her brow and narrowed her eyes. As loudly as she could manage without drawing too much attention, she said, "Tell her to leave it. I'm sure she's got great insurance."

I heard Shari's frantic voice slipping through my fingers, so I pressed the phone back up to my mouth and said, "Maybe it would just be good to get out of there quickly. Don't worry about your stuff."

"Don't worry about my stuff?" she moaned. "That might be easy to say when all that's really yours is an Ikea desk and a hand-me-down mattress," and I couldn't tell if that was geared more toward me or Leanne or both of us.

"Tell her that we're on vacation," Leanne spat. "Hell, tell her that we're in god damned Peru."

I frowned at Leanne and said, "She knows where we are."

But I heard Shari shouting through the receiver so I put it back to my ear to catch the tail end of, ". . . so there's time to get here. Just get in your car and come straight to my place."

Leanne was opening and closing a fist in front of me, either indicating that she wanted the phone, wanted to hit me, or wanted to hit Shari through the phone.

I covered up the receiver again and said, "Listen, what if I just head up there for the day, help her out, and come back down by tonight? We've got the cottage for a couple more days and you should stay with Runt anyway."

"Give. Me. The. Phone," Leanne said. "I'm going to tell her that you're quitting. This is too much, Jacob. It's insane."

I pulled the phone away from her reach and heard Shari crackling through the speaker. "Give it here," Leanne said, looking so tense that I could see a small vein bubbling through the skin around her temple. "I mean it, Jacob. You can't work for this woman anymore."

"No," I snapped back. "I'm not doing that."

Leanne set a hand on her hip and said, "You're a personal assistant, Jacob. It's not like you're giving up the presidency."

And without fully knowing where it came from or whether or not I truly felt that way, I said, "And you're a fucking preschool teacher. You change diapers for a living."

"I'm sure she'll be having you do just that once she's aged another ten years," Leanne spat.

We stared at each other, huffing, and I put the phone to my mouth and said, "I'll be there soon. It shouldn't be more than an hour if the traffic isn't bad."

Shari said, "Thank you! Thank you! I promise I'll make it up to you!"

I hung up the phone and Leanne sank into her seat. "You told her that you'd be there in less than an hour if the traffic wasn't bad," and Leanne laughed. "Well guess what, Jacob? The traffic is going to be fucking bad. The road is going to be fucking closed. You think they're going to let you just drive into a place that's being evacuated? You think you can just pull up to a roadblock, flash your personal assistant's badge, and be let in? Or maybe, just maybe you'll beat the shit out of the firemen, hijack their truck, and stave off the blaze all by yourself."

I started to say something, but Leanne, clearly fueled by the fact that everything she had suspected seemed to be coming true, said, "Now that would be truly worthy of a raise!"

"Leanne," I pleaded. "I'm coming back. I promise."

But she only shook her head and said, "Oh no. If you leave now, you better do all you can to keep that house from burning, because you're going to need a place to stay."

The interstate went to shit just outside of Buda. I saw red and blue lights flashing up ahead. A huddle of uniformed officers herding people off at the nearest exit. My phone kept buzzing in my cup holder and, looking down at it, I expected Leanne to have called at least once. But yet again, it was Shari.

"Hey," I said, before she should get a word in, "I'm on my way but they've got roadblocks up everywhere."

Shari said, "You didn't take 35, did you?"

I sighed. "Yes, but I'm getting off now."

I could hear her oozing disappointment through the receiver and I couldn't help but think about how much that would have satisfied Leanne.

Edging my way over to the right lane as Shari instructed me about how to take the back roads west into Driftwood and up through Cypress Hill and into her neighborhood, I began to wonder just how much stock I should be putting into her advice at all. I thought about simply turning around and telling Leanne that I'd had a change of heart, but part of me knew she'd smell it on me. The lie.

I said, "Is Driftwood being evacuated too?"

"Listen," Shari said. It was how she always started off a sentence when she was going to explain how simply something could work. "Just get up here as fast as you can and I'll be sure to send you and Leanne away on an all-expense paid trip to wherever you can think of. Hell, I'll send you all the way to Kukui. You know where that is? Maui. It's beautiful. Never stops raining there. You couldn't spark a match if you tried."

I thought about telling Shari that Leanne wasn't in the car with me, but it seemed pathetic. Or maybe too personal. It was odd to think that somewhere else in the world, the sky wasn't filling with soot and ash and smoke. That the soil was damp and lush with fungus and old growth, although I think I'd always heard something about how fires were beneficial in some way. That flames were just a catalyst to a whole new life. "Sure," I told Shari, angling my car off the highway and onto the feeder road. "Whatever you say."

"You would just love it," she exclaimed. "There's a great little Marriott right there on the water." And from the way she talked, it sounded as if she could already envision us there, no pets or girlfriends allowed, our faces reflected in rain-soaked windows gazing out on the waves of the Pacific. "They have the best Mahi-mahi you can find. It's exquisite," she said, like she wasn't even in danger anymore. Like there was no need to worry. Like there was simply water as far as the eye could see. Just water, water everywhere. ❧

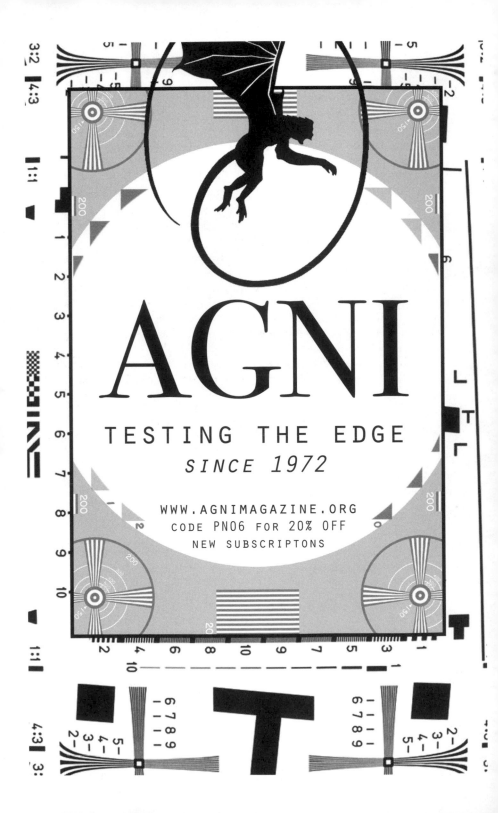

AGNI

TESTING THE EDGE

SINCE 1972

WWW.AGNIMAGAZINE.ORG
CODE PN06 FOR 20% OFF
NEW SUBSCRIPTONS

Gravel Road

Adam J. Gellings

after Frank Stanford

That night my childhood dog,
Shadow, woke me from a dream.

I stood up & looked out the window

I saw you was dancin'
in the gravel road like Aphrodite
untying your sandal
searching for a flea

I saw your clothes crawl off

I saw there was a lizard
or a snake
that bit your heel.
Blood stain on your leather sole.

I saw that soulless bitch dog barking

   Speak up
   Speak up
   Speak up

   Speak up at my father

rottin' like a persimmon
in his rocking chair
I saw the upholstery was stained.

I felt the clouds float by us
in the dead of night

like a line of trout

I saw Ben Holt was still alive
sittin' next to me
drinkin' PBRs
on the midnight patio

I saw kamikaze moths
whizzin' into a hushing
yellow bulb

I waved to Uncle Kip
workin' the fields
under a husk of moon

his hand slippin' into the corn
grinder

I saw the blood run
through the shaking kernels
like cherry cola

his four fingertips twitchin'
in the spreading stain
scarin' away
the gnats

I saw him keep moving
like nothin' ever happened
like nothin'
ever happened
like he just kept pushin' on

I saw the stars streak over
like a thousand
scalpels ripping
open the goddamn sky

the moon
was just a lemon wedge
hangin' there
hangin' over everything

squeezin' us
into the stinging cracks
of the black

erupting

gunpowder of night.

The Gymnastics Teacher

Adam J. Gellings

is no more
than five feet one inches tall.
She wants you to know

that kids much bigger than you
have broken her nose.

She wants you to see
her scowl is a second skin.

Deteriorating leather,
aged & oiled from exposure,
the pocket worn thin.

Another day of pink metallic
leotards & blue mats
pushed in a pile
pumping blue blood
& nicotine through the veins
of her outstretched arm.

Another day of small bodies
whirling through warm,
stale air.

It's been fifteen years, but
she does not want to sit still.

It's been fifteen years, but
she does not want you
to know
she can't sleep at night.

That she eats alone. That she needs
whiskey to even show up
each morning.

She wants you to show her
what *you* can do.
With your arms bent.

She wants you to show her
what you can do.
With your arms straight.

She wants you to strut around
& vaunt as she did
when she was younger.

To dance to the end
of the beam.
To roll & tumble to the edge
of the canvas.
To tunnel your way
through a maze
of fireflies.

She wants you to turn three paces
toward the sun & set in motion
a series of smiles.

She doesn't know fatigue.
She never loved him.

She wants you to know
that kids much bigger than you

have broken her nose.
She wants you to
jump off.

One at a time.

Jump off.

Remember Us Now, Wandering

Jess E. Jelsma

Down along the Rio Grande, where the orange canyon levels out to rocky sand, you and I meet the singing Mexican. We've almost lost the trail when we spot him, his feet planted wide and his voice a hollow note in the echoing chasm. I motion for us to go ahead, begin the steep slope up the path that leads away from the riverbed, but you want to stay and watch him. Standing there beside his mare, the horse's flanks so thin that we can see the outline of all eighteen of her ribs, the man sings as if he means to make some meaning of the split that divides us from him—of the Rio's depths, shallow enough for even my short legs to cross over and over again.

He sings, *¿Donde debago de estas arenas son los huesos de mis padres?* and later, when we are both tucked together like nesting dolls in our small nylon tent, you can't stop repeating the words back to me in English.

Where? you ask as you zip your sleeping bag open and hang the lantern up by its black braided strap. *Where beneath these sands are the bones of my parents?*

You whisper the question over and over again as the lantern's bulb grows dim, as outside the moon rises so bright that, at first, we are sure another car must have turned in. Lying with my ear pressed to the damp side of the tent, I listen to the wind that rises out there on the plains, to the approaching dust storm that will unearth all the metal stakes we have buried deep in the clay.

Where, you ask, are they? and I wait for some sort of answer as the night bleeds into day, as I sleep with my eyes shut tight against the desert's lonely caterwauling.

In the confines of the mountain basin, there is a small white cross that we take note of on our first expedition. You have your backpack hoisted high on your shoulders, your forearms and neck already pink with sunburn, and I stoop to examine the letters that have been painted there on the wood. I read out, *Juan de Leon*, and though we scour our guidebook for some mention of the man, we find no firm identity to settle on.

You suggest, *Maybe he wanted to be buried out here in the basin*, but I can't stop picturing what the heat of the desert would do to a body, how quickly the flesh would purple and bloat before falling away.

Shot right off his horse, the cashier at the camp store tells us. We have stopped by to wash our feet in the bathroom sink, our ankles swollen and bruised from the six-mile hike. *Used the guy for target practice. At least, that's what I think.*

The man's skin is grizzled and unevenly pigmented, a white scar stretched high across one cheek and his right index finger missing from a one year stint in Vietnam. He has spent the last forty years traveling the most desolate landscapes in the country, from the Hundred-Mile Wilderness to the Nebraska Sand Hills and now the sullen deserts of West Texas.

Body was so decayed when they found him out there, it had to be buried on the spot.

We are quiet as he rings up a pair of baseball hats to stave off the sun, as he hands us a brochure warning of the dangers of heat stroke and dehydration, as he rubs at his nose with the stump of his foreshortened finger.

I'm telling you. They only had a few scraps of clothes left to identify him.

Back at our campsite, we lie beneath the blue tarp we have rigged between two stunted cottonwoods, and I wonder if it was the vultures or the wolves who got the last look at him—Juan's face a smooth plain before his cheeks hollowed and his brow began to disintegrate. Was it a man from town who shot him down that day, some gringo with the same dust-riddled skin and sunbaked hands of all those who live along the borderlands?

Probably shot in the back, you say, your hands casting looming shadows down on my legs. *The poor bastard never even saw it coming.*

We are on our way to the Hot Springs when we come across the signs warning of a recent uptick in thefts and muggings. I lock our wallets in the glove compartment while you change, your hiking pants exchanged for a pair of navy swim trunks and all the blonde downy hair revealed on your legs.

Along the trail, we stop to read the placards about the old bathhouse once run by J.O. Langford, a sick man driven out west in search of a cure-all hidden deep within the desert. He built a motor park here beside the magical springs—seven stone cabins and a brushwood bathing shelter to cure the weary of their rheumatism and stomach trouble and skin disease.

Now, the buildings stand to rot as does the metal gate at the nearby border crossing, and we walk slowly down the path through the thick encroaching reeds, through the grasses that rise so high as to block out all but the gray, cloud-streaked vista overhead.

The water is a steady one hundred and five degrees where it seeps from the springs' stone foundation. A fellow traveler has wedged a thermometer there in the century-old masonry, the cracked glass tube languidly leaking a diluted stream of mercury, but I take the flush that rises to our skin as proof more than anything. I sit there beside you as our legs color pink and then red, as our chests deflate and balloon, as the Rio winds past as it was always meant to do.

If there is a danger that lurks there upon the opposite shore, it is one that resides somewhere deep beneath the warbler's humming—beyond the rustle of a small javelina as she noses her snout into the water, behind the calm static drone of the cicadas.

You wrap your arm around my waist and ask me, *Are you scared?*

Peering through the grasses, I think of all that we cannot see: the Mexican black bears and the collared peccary and the dense amber coats of the coyotes. I imagine all of those who have tried to make a life here only to be displaced: of the Chisos who gave way to the Spanish presidios and the buffalo soldiers and the ranchers with their sheep and goats that overgrazed and overgrazed.

From within the springs, you pull out a grub that has been blackened and baked.

No. Not yet, I say.

There was once a wax factory here along the Great Comanche Trail, or so our guidebook proclaims. The workers were paid only a dollar a day—Mexican men hired to cut down the candelilla stalks and boil the stems, to add sulfuric acid to the raging concoction until the wax rose to the surface as a scalding, pliable skin. Skimmed from the top, the substance was boiled again, the wax rendered with steam and sweat and each worker's red, blistered flesh.

Hiking along a dried out creek bed, I can't imagine how one could live— plumes of suffocating, wet heat lingering atop the desert for days on end—but you take the guidebook from me and read out what happened to the camp.

The whole factory was burned in a raid, you say, your finger tapping down hard on the glossy page. *Nearly roasted those men alive when the bandits came.*

Now, there are no rust-laden boilers or ruins to mark the place of decay, and I wonder about the fire that must have consumed the place, the flames catching quickly across the dry sotol and the hard-spined agave. Throughout these one hundred miles of land, there has long been a burn ban, and we both know what even a hint of a spark could do to bring an end to all of life here in the basin.

Water is in short supply in the backlands, and we walk the trail with our baseball hats pulled down low against the sun, our lips raw and chapped from the desert's ever-circulating layer of dust. I suck in my cheeks and try to summon a modicum of spit, but find that my tongue is sore and limp, my throat so parched that I can barely speak up.

It's just a little bit farther, you say, glancing over your shoulder to check on me, and I pray that we are close to the end, that some salvation will come here on the dirt road between Glenn Springs and Pine Canyon.

Afterward on the car ride back to our tent, I make you pull over so I can dry heave beside a lone fragrant sumac.

You ask, *Are you ok?* but crouched down on my hands and knees, my palms covered in grit, I can only shake my head, my skin starved for the sweat that refuses to come.

On our hike up to Emory Peak, we hear that there is a wind advisory in effect.

Nearly blew me right off the trail, a fellow hiker says, his hair a mess of tangled curls and his pupils glassy and dilated. He has the same gaunt look as many of the other drifters we have met out here in the basin: his bones sharp beneath his skin, a constellation of track marks dotting his sunburned forearm. Camping is a cheap way to live, many of the young men hiking in with little more than a sleeping bag, and I wonder if there is anyone out there looking for them, what it would mean to find this teen sprawled out six-hundred feet below the peak with his delicate skull crushed in.

He'll be ok, you say as if to reassure me of the other hiker's safety, but it is us I fear for as we climb higher and higher in elevation, as the wind tears at my t-shirt and whips your pants around your legs.

You carry a gallon jug today, your backpack off-kilter and heavy, but no amount of water can save me from the panic slowly swelling inside my chest, from the numbness that creeps first over my arms and then my hands, from the white static noise filling my head. As we climb, I cling to the sparse tufts of scrub grass that populate the sand, to the rock face that turns slick with our perspiration, to whatever I can hold onto against the wind.

Around us, the vistas gradually begin to open—the earth a glowing canvas of orange and soda green and red—and my legs are shaking and wet with sweat, my breath short as we push on to the final ascent.

At the peak, the valley spreads out before us like the map we once studied at the very beginning of our journey, the desert reduced to a flat, surmountable plain. Across the way, the Rio winds like an extant vein along the borderlands, and I cry not because of all that I have heard or seen, but because I am finally scared of something.

It's all right, you say. *We can go back down again.*

But there are bones, I want to tell you, buried deep beneath this sand—so many sets of them that not even you or I could ever begin to understand.

Perhaps, I say, *we are both safer here on the mountain.* ❧

What Guy Says No?

Jennifer Genest

Doug walked, rain spitting on his sweatshirt hood and his long hair, toward the rectory. He had never gone to confession—never had his first communion. Last night, after it had happened, he ran back to the river and dragged Carrie out, pulled her onto the bank to keep her dry, pushed the corn-silk hair from her face and tried to breathe into the lips he had been kissing just moments before. He hated himself for never being a Boy Scout, never learning how to save anyone but himself.

He knocked on the back door of the rectory and his Uncle Raphael emerged in the white collar and black clothes. "Doug! What a surprise! Come in!"

Everything in the rectory was old but pristine: an aqua-colored table from the 50s with chrome edges. Waxed floors and well-oiled cabinets. The smell of furniture polish. His uncle poured a glass of ginger ale for Doug. "I have a couple arriving soon," he said, "To talk to me about their engagement. But why don't you sit here, read the paper while you wait?"

Doug would have to do it fast. He looked his uncle in the eyes. "Can I go to confession?" he said. "I mean, right now? I don't really know how..."

"Of course," his uncle said. "But wouldn't you like another priest?"

"With you," Doug said. "It has to be with you." He hadn't seen his uncle in a year, not since his father—Uncle Raphael's brother—had gone to jail for dealing. Now Doug lived with his stepmother, Sylvia, who called Raphael a phony. She said he was not a man of God; he was a man of staring at her ass. Not that Doug could blame him.

"I'd be happy to listen if you're comfortable with me," Raphael said, "But I have this appointment in a minute, and I want to make sure we have enough time..."

"I...I killed someone," Doug blurted. "A girl. This girl. Sort of my girlfriend. Nobody knew we were dating. She didn't want anyone to know." They hadn't been dating; they'd been sneaking around drinking rum he'd stolen from Sylvia. It was the only reason Carrie liked him.

The ice popped in the ginger ale, sinking lower in the glass. Uncle Raphael blinked rapidly. "Doug," he said, "Stop."

"I didn't mean to," Doug said. He leaned forward, pushed his face into his hands. "I didn't mean to."

Raphael held his hand up. "Stop talking, please. Let's go to the confessional. This isn't the way to do this..."

But it was done. The rectory doorbell rang and Doug stood.

"Stay," his uncle said. "I'll tell this couple I need to reschedule. I'll be right back."

Before Raphael could return, Doug slipped out the back door and cut through the mini-mart parking lot. He would go to Fitzy's for now, grab a beer, get his nerve up and his temper down before going back to Sylvia's—hopefully she was alone now. He remembered what Sylvia felt like under her red satin nightie—the weight of her breasts, the softness of her belly and legs; for years he had wished for her and lately, when she was drunk, she let him into her bed, said she would teach him how to love a woman—and she had, without ever taking his pants off. In fact, she hadn't touched him at all—only kissed.

Surely she knew his secret—that there was nothing under his jeans worth seeing, that it was just a mangled little mess, that no amount of juice or protein shakes or muscles would change. He was born this way and he was used to hiding it; he had never used a urinal, always the bathroom stall at school and kids made fun of him for it. His father never spoke of it to Doug, but he probably had to Sylvia; there was no way of knowing now and he sure wasn't going to ask her.

Doug had dropped out of twelfth grade this year; he hated school, and having a job—even if it was janitor and snack bar guy at Roller Kingdom—meant he paid the rent for Sylvia, like a real man.

It was still raining out as he walked to Fitzy's and he could smell the dank amber river water—you could smell it almost everywhere in this town. The river made him replay every event last night and he cringed: he had come home from lifting weights at Fitzy's, grabbed a Pop Tart and a Diet Pepsi for Sylvia so they could watch *Entertainment Tonight*, and walked into her room. He opened the door to the horror of sheets and bodies humping so hard they never turned to notice him standing there; Sylvia's red toenails peeking out of the blankets, the back of a man whose face he never saw—just a tattoo of the Tasmanian Devil on his shoulder. When Doug saw this in a split second, he decided that if Sylvia could fuck around, so could he.

Carrie was fifteen. She was the only girl who had ever flirted with him and she was delicate and beautiful, like a Christmas tree angel. He knew she was using him for alcohol—she never wanted them to be seen in public together because she said he was "too old" for her—but still, it felt pretty awesome to have her wink at him every time she came to Open Skate on Friday nights. From behind the snack bar, he would smile, pour some of Sylvia's rum he had hidden in his Pepsi bottle into Carrie's blue Slush Puppy, and bring it to her while she skated. She liked to flirt with him, invited him over and even tried to kiss him—but he was too scared. But last night, after he walked in on Sylvia, he grabbed Sylvia's entire bottle and put it in the inner pocket of his jean jacket. Then he ran to Carrie's house.

Carrie lived with her Gramma, but it was easy to knock on the door without her Gramma even hearing; she was half-deaf and kept the television up so loud you couldn't think. He'd simply raised the bottle when Carrie came to the door and smirked at her. "Want to get wasted?"

They walked into the woods and down one of the dirt-bike paths, passing the bottle back and forth, as the rum put a strange, thin cloud over his anger. They both giggled. Soon they approached a sheep farm where a dozen or so black and white sheep grazed behind a crumbling rock wall. Barbed wire had been staked behind the wall to keep the sheep in. Dense packs of spruce and pine and young oaks hid them from the sheep and the farmhouse in the distance. If you paid attention, you could see that the path forked here—one led further up The Ridge, up to The Leap, and one was overgrown. Doug pushed aside the low pine branches and tall leaning weeds and led Carrie into the hidden place.

A few feet in front of them was parked a perfectly square, small, red wooden house on wheels, its hitch resting on a large rock. It had a picture window on one side with white shutters, and underneath was painted, in candy-cane-striped letters, "SANTA'S HUT." Green curtains were drawn shut inside. He wondered if Carrie was as fascinated as he had been a couple of weeks ago, when, on his way back from a Leap party, he'd spied its redness through the leaves. This was where Santa's Hut went after they took it away from town square! He felt like he was in on a huge secret. It felt like it was his because he found it.

Carrie's eyebrows were raised. His heart sped as he waited for her to laugh at him. He was so pathetic. Why didn't he have a car?

Carrie started to laugh, but she didn't seem to be laughing at Doug. "Santa's Hut!"

Doug laughed too. Should he just play it off as a joke? Was she going to go along with this?

But he didn't have to think anymore; Carrie grabbed his neck and started kissing him.

He slid the latch on the hut's door and led her in.

"I feel like I'm in a dollhouse," she said.

Santa's throne-like chair was made of plywood painted gold and white and turned out to be immovable; there was barely enough room to lie on the carpet between the throne and the picture window.

He never imagined any girl would want to kiss him at all, never mind this much. The kissing didn't stop as they sat on the throne together. She slid her cool hands under his shirt and over his chest, making him shiver. He knew his chest was hard and muscled and he hoped she'd stay there. She traced the waist of his jeans, sliding her fingertip across the band of his boxers. He held her hands, guiding them up to his neck. He sucked on her fingers. He started to feel dizzy with the rum and the intensity of wanting to get her clothes off and show her what he could do.

He removed her bra and held her breasts in his hands, surprised by how small and high and firm these fleshy parts of her were. It was all so different from Sylvia that it was almost shocking, so different that all he could do was try to block out the predictable, comfortable things his hands were used to, breasts that had substance not feather, breasts that could smother him. Not like this. Not like this at all.

But *this* was better, wasn't it? This was a girl who followed him here, a girl who was into him.

Hands shaking, he tried for her pants. She freed his ponytail from its band and raked his dark hair in her hands. She giggled, suddenly seeming very drunk. "No," she said, holding his hands back from her zipper. "Let me . . . *see* you." She drew her shoulders up and held them for a moment in a shy shrug.

He hid his instant of horror by bowing his head to the side and letting his hair cover his face. Nausea washed over him and his pulse quickened. He suddenly wanted to leave, wished he'd never met her, wanted more than anything for this to be Sylvia, not this stupid *girl* . . . this girl who didn't know what she was doing.

She kissed him, tugging at his pants again. He held her arms more solidly. She laughed at first. "Come on," she said. "I've never . . . done this, anything but kiss . . . I just want to look . . ."

"I can make you feel *good*, Carrie . . ." But when he heard his voice saying her name it sounded so unnatural that it stopped whatever had been driving him to prove this to her. He stood and pulled his tee shirt down.

"What's the matter?" She started to laugh. "What guy says no?" She began to giggle, nudging him in the hip.

"Come on," he said. "Let's get out of here."

She grabbed his hand and he yanked it away. She looked strange, standing there, her breasts so small and white and stark against the green curtain. She was so young. She was fucking with him, playing with him. He looked down at the carpet because he now felt sick looking at her. This wasn't going to work. There was no woman in the world that was going to get this. Why had he thought this could work?

"You should put your shirt on," he said. "Let's get going."

Carrie's face dropped. For a flash of a second she looked like she might cry. Then she smirked at him and held her arm across her breasts while she picked her shirt up off of Santa's chair. "What are you, gay?" she said.

He raised an eyebrow. "I'm not fuckin' gay."

"Well, I'm not some stupid kid."

"I never said . . ."

"I've never heard of a guy saying *no* before."

"I thought you said you never done this before."

"I haven't, but still. I never heard of it."

He tried to calm down. His head was blurry and he wished for a second that he were a little less drunk. She was quiet as she turned from him to pull her shirt on.

They made their way along the path. Carrie tried to hold his hand but he put them in his jacket pockets. It started to thunder and sprinkle rain as they approached the brook. He knew he ought to at least help her across because she was so drunk.

He crossed first and then held his hand out to her. She took it, smiled, and stepped carefully across the wet rocks. She hopped off the last rock and into his arms, pushing her chest against his and trying to kiss him. For a moment it didn't seem so bad and he let her, but then he knew again that there would be no way to get her to stop so he held her wrists. "Let's go," he said.

She shook her wrists free, wobbling, and then slapped him so fast he didn't even see it.

He touched his jaw; it was hot where she'd struck him but then the heat started to tighten his neck and travel to the small aching center of his chest where every breath and swallow seemed to be trapped.

She stepped back once, standing again with both of her sneakers on the last slippery rock. Her brows were knit in a combination of anger and pain, and then, again, the smirk. "You know what?" she slurred. "You're . . . you must be *small*." She snapped her fingers loosely and shook her wet hair off her shoulders. "That's it, isn't it? It must be *tiny*, like a little . . . a *tiny* little . . . "

But she didn't have time to finish. He slapped her so hard that blood flew from her lip in a string onto the leaves and mud. She fell backward into the brook with a plunging splash, her head meeting a rock with a wet cracking sound, and then she was still.

"Carrie?" he said. His hands were tense at his sides.

There was no answer, just the teasingly gentle pat-pat of raindrops on firm papery oak leaves, of the brook babbling, of what felt like his cells screaming down to the marrow.

When he looked back on this, he realized there had been time: Time to reach in and scoop Carrie out, time to rub her cheeks and wait for her to regain consciousness, time to apologize. He could have carried her to the farmhouse and said his friend had fallen in the brook and needed stitches. He could even have just knocked on the door and abandoned her like a litter of kittens, because she didn't even want anyone to know that she knew him.

Instead he just stood there. He didn't know how long he had stayed there with her but it was long enough for him to crouch down and wash his hands near her feet. He watched as her hair floated up around her sinking face and the dark water covered everything.

He walked quickly from the rectory now, toward Fitzy's. Fitzy was his only friend; they lifted in his basement—they made their own weights by filling five-pound coffee cans with concrete and sticking them on either end of an old pipe. They used this for squats and presses. Fitzy taught him how to make protein shakes and do steroids. Fitzy's parents made him go to Catholic school and he had to go to confession once a week, so Doug knew from him that a priest could not ever—under any circumstances—tell anyone what he heard in confession.

Fitzy was splitting wood in his parent's driveway. He looked up at Doug. "Hey, dumbass," he said. "You look like hell. Jesus, you almost look green."

"I've been sick."

"Yeah? Hung over?"

"Nah. Just sick. Flu." Doug watched him balance a section of log on a big stump, swing the ax, and split it in two.

"Why'd you come here then, asshole?" Fitzy said, "If you're contagious?"

"I don't think it's contagious anymore." His heart began to pound as he led up to it. "Hey remember I told you my uncle is a priest?" Doug said. "I saw him today. I even went to confession." Somehow, despite what he had confessed, this felt like a rite of passage—one he hadn't earned, but one that put him as equal with Fitzy, who had a religious education. Doug's own father was raised that way, but he never brought Doug to mass—he could remember his father claiming to be "anti-Catholic," whatever that meant. For Doug now, telling someone he had confessed felt necessary—even if he couldn't say what his sin was.

Fitzy paused and leaned the ax on the ground. "That's a sacrament. You haven't even had the Eucharist. How'd you do that?"

"I just talked to him."

"Oh, so you didn't actually go to *confession*-confession—in the church?"

"No, man, he's my uncle. We just talked."

"I hope you didn't tell him about shoplifting that six-pack last week," Fitzy laughed. "Don't tell him nothing illegal; he can report it if it isn't real confession."

Doug blanched. "Shut up," he said, forcing a laugh. He began to get dizzy.

"Really," Fitzy said, suddenly serious. "It has to be a ritual. This shit has to be official if you want to be Catholic. You can't just sit down and shoot the shit on someone's couch and call it confession. That's why mafia guys always go to confession. Actual confession. Then they're protected."

Doug's throat tightened. He picked up a piece of split wood. "You got a beer?" he asked. "I'll help you stack." He arranged the wood in the pile against the garage.

"Go home," Fitzy said. "Go to bed, man, you look like hell. Take some fuckin' Nyquil."

He got back to Sylvia's and let the front screen door slap to announce his arrival. The air was moist with the scent of her coconut shampoo; she had just showered. She sat in her silk robe watching *The Price Is Right*, combing her damp, dark red hair. "Hey dummy," she said affectionately. There was no indication that she knew he'd seen her last night. "Where ya been?"

Doug hung up his jacket. "Fitzy's."

She studied him as he sat next to her on the old denim couch they had rescued from garbage. It still smelled like the Lysol spray they had soaked it with. She rubbed his forearm admiringly. "I can see the workouts are paying off," she said sweetly. She rested her head on his shoulder, like nothing had happened. Like last night had been imagined. All at once, he forgave her.

She picked up the remote. "Want to watch the news?"

Anything but the news, he thought. He knew Carrie's grandmother was probably frantic for her by now. He took the remote from her hand and put it on the blue milk crate they used as a coffee table. "I saw my uncle today," he said.

"Oh?"

"I don't think he's such a bad guy, do you?" Doug wanted her to tell him he was trustworthy. Loyal. More loyal to family than to the church.

"You don't know everything about your uncle," she said. "I told you he's a phony."

"Is he the kind of guy you can trust?" Doug asked, flat-out.

Sylvia coughed and grinned. "Your father didn't trust him. He does things just to impress people. He used to smoke, drink his ass off, and get tattoos, even—all to impress *me*, you know. I think he even became a priest to impress people, with all this holier-than-thou bullshit. But he still has an angel on one shoulder, a devil on the other—same as the rest of us."

She loosened the silken tie from her robe and brought his hand to her breast. He couldn't respond: the words "tattoo" and "devil" rang in his ears and a loud, electrical buzz filled his head. He would lose Sylvia if he asked her who she was with last night. He fought between his gut and reason: she hated Uncle Raphael. She wouldn't do that. Things were fine. Things hadn't changed.

Sylvia took his other hand and touched his fingertips to her mouth. He closed his eyes but his face and body were rigid.

"What's wrong, baby?" she asked softly.

He began to shake. He said he thought he was getting a fever.

She stroked his hair, her red fingernails lightly scratching his scalp, and paused to turn the channel to the news. He listened to it as she bent in to kiss him. He waited for the report of a missing girl. He waited for someone to come forward or withhold. He prayed, for the first time in his life, that nobody would admit to knowing him. ⮞

In Elixir

Tanya Grae

In the bottom of a mason jar, anyone—

                        mermaid or sailor—

can get caught in a net with starfish, sea glass,

& the silver line of hooks.

                 How a lure intoxicates

under its crooked moon. I forget discretion, to shelter my thoughts

with a smile. Transparent creatures of the ocean

                           have no expression

in their lulling way. If we pretend they're benign & don't sting,

they don't dissolve—

               the fullness of Pandora's *pithos*

pouring to say what we want isn't what is, but if it was

we'd be immortal.

              Shine can blind a person

in one drink & sink the dark right into their deep.

How our passions maroon us.

                  An hourglass of sugar turns to salt—

a mouthful of pinion, rudder, course.

                    We enter naked

& take on form. There are no wings while we walk—

folded, dormant, beating,

            disguised as a pulse.

Rewind

Tanya Grae

I look for what keeps me here,
that first love & breathlessness
my therapist compares to crack—

that high when I don't give a fuck,
when I feel like I've won, when I am
solid & safe & lightness, that *yes*—

To stay here is Hollywood & celluloid
reel, flammable, wound so tight
a fingernail can't wedge between

then & now, a spool of darkness
I replay when nothing catches,
when my prayer beads move

under thumb faster & faster, when
the bike pedals outpace the chain,
when all the plates I'm spinning drop

& ring the house to silence—
that flood of light
when the movie burns.

CLOUD ATLAS by David Mitchell

Robert Burke Warren

All avid readers have a story wherein a book seeks them out. Over the course of, say, twenty-four hours, three unconnected people will mention the same book, saying, "You must read this." Then, and only then, you'll see a copy on an end table, and yet another person will say, "I just finished that. It's right up your alley. Take it." And/or you'll be strolling aimlessly through a bookstore or library, and after having discussed the book, its spine will pop into your field of vision. You succumb to a pleasant sense of inevitability. You read it, and it rearranges your molecular structure. This is how it is with David Mitchell's *Cloud Atlas* and me.

Cloud Atlas, however, is not my first David Mitchell. That distinction belongs to *The Thousand Autumns of Jacob de Zoet*, from 2010. I learn of this book from Mitchell himself. He is speaking on *Fresh Air*. I've never heard of him. His voice captivates me. Because he is an Irishman who overcame a stutter and married a Japanese woman, his delivery is distinctive, like he's from his own country, which he kind of is. Anyway, within a day or so of this radio spot, I stumble on a profile of him in the *New York Times* magazine. (Kudos to his publicist.) The profile mentions the real-life manmade island of Dejima, off the coast of Nagasaki, where much of the novel's action transpires. There are photos of Mitchell with his wife and son, and a picture of the island. My fascination with *Jacob de Zoet* deepens. The next day, by chance, I see the gorgeous dust jacket on a bookseller's shelf. I've got a little time, so I stand there, reading the first chapter, to see if it grabs me. It does. I purchase and devour the book, a historical novel set in 1799, a love story between a red haired man from the Dutch East India Co., and a brilliant, beautiful, disfigured Japanese woman he can never possess. The sentences are lovely, the prose musical, the plot captivating. The history is a bonus. Multiple points of view motor it along. The soul of the book shimmers. *The Thousand Autumns of Jacob de Zoet* makes me want to be a better writer.

Unbeknownst to me, I am entering Mitchell's "ur-novel." I.e., he has since acknowledged that all his meaty, ambitious books—produced with astonishing regularity—are connected. Although not immediately obvious, his oeuvre is a sprawling, storied multiverse of willpower, subtle magic, human monstrousness, science, and love. Even, perish the thought, *romance.* Characters from one book make cameos in others. The ur-novel spans eras. Yet, each individual book stands alone, too. I almost don't want to contemplate this. It's a bit much.

As I'm loaning *Jacob de Zoet* to a notoriously opinionated friend, he says, "Looking forward to this, but really, *Cloud Atlas* is Mitchell's magnum opus. You gotta read that." I vaguely recall the *NYT* piece mentioning *Cloud Atlas* as a book of interconnected stories in wildly different styles, spread over eras, a microcosm of the aforementioned ur-novel. It sounds complicated and arty, and I am hesitant. *Jacob de Zoet* isn't really that complex. It's an easy elevator pitch, eminently accessible.

No matter. *Cloud Atlas* has marked me, apparently. The next day, after I read somewhere about the Wachowskis' (*Matrix* creators) imminent *Cloud Atlas* movie, *I see the book on a library shelf.* It's a well-worn hardcover edition (it's been out for about six years), dog-eared, radiating lit love, traces of multiple readers' breath and sweat on the pages. *Fine, I say, I will read two fat Mitchell books back-to-back.* I vow to finish the novel before the movie version premieres. Deadlines are good. But this one is unnecessary. I finish it in a few days, screaming from my bed, "I love this book! This book is so great!"

Why the screaming? What is happening? At this point I must try to describe what it is about *Cloud Atlas* that put me in the position of saying, when asked what my favorite book is: "*Cloud Atlas.*" I've tried several times to do this, *voce a voce*, and for the most part, my listeners' eyes glaze. Nevertheless:

You think you know how a story unfolds inside you. You've read a lot, and yes, authors employ myriad styles of revelation of character and plot, but the forms are somewhat predictable, and you feel them within you in a specific place. Not so with *Cloud Atlas*. It is a collection of "nested" stories. Although not immediately apparent, characters are reading or telling or writing or archiving the stories, each of which ends abruptly in the first half of the book, causing initial feelings of discomfort and confusion. But then, in reverse order, Mitchell finishes each story in the second half; that's when they connect, and confusion turns slowly, then increasingly, to revelation. The narratives unfold like rose petals. Mitchell reveals them as all part of one story of love and daring and courage across the ages, from the 19th century to a near, and then a far, dystopian future. The stakes go from personal to global. Each protagonist, it turns out, is a reincarnation of a specific soul, moving through time, tempted and touched by both destructive and productive forces. I do not know this as I read, but it doesn't matter. I intuit a connection across the narratives, and it pulls me through, and then the payoff is huge. My "intuition center," wherever that is, gets goosed.

Derring-do of form aside, the content of the stories is rich, filled with drama and believable, relatable characters you root for (or loathe). But you do not apprehend the connective tissue until about midway through, and you feel you're learning to read all over again. A sense of wonder blooms as a newly lit place within you appreciates *story.*

I do not expect to feel that while reading a book again. At least not in this life. ❧

An Element of Blank:
Figuring Pain in Graphic Narrative

Thomas Dolinger

Pain, writes Emily Dickinson, has "an Element of Blank": "It cannot recollect / When it begun – Or if there were / A time when it was not."[1] In *The Hospital Suite* (2014), a graphic pathography drawn in the sparest of lines, cartoonist John Porcellino literalizes this world-destroying blank. His intestinal tumor not yet diagnosed, Porcellino draws himself writhing helplessly in a hospital bed. "I was delerious [*sic*] with pain," reads one panel. Below is a disembodied pair of eyes, quietly pleading with the reader. The next panel is not a panel at all, but the comics equivalent of Dickinson's searingly eloquent dash:

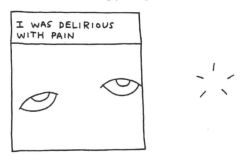

Undone by pain, the body—and, with it, the visual substructure of the narrative world—disappears. If comics is, as Hillary Chute has argued, a "procedure of . . . embodiment," then Porcellino's illness narrative records the gradual erasure of the drawn body and its neatly bounded world.[2]

And yet that hurting body inevitably reappears: the "Element of Blank" gives way to another line of verse, another panel. As I trace this pattern of figuration and dissolution, I'm guided by a simple question: how does the art form we know as comics render the felt experience of physical pain? This question opens onto others: what features of pain does graphic narrative emphasize or occlude? Is the phenomenology of pain merely another facet of a broader illness experience, or does it demand more specific forms of artistic and critical attention? As attention to Porcellino's *Hospital Suite* reveals, comics represents an especially

---

1 *Emily Dickinson*, The Poems of Emily Dickinson, *ed. R.W. Franklin (Cambridge, MA: Harvard University Press, 1999), 339-40.*

2 *John Porcellino*, The Hospital Suite *(Montreal: Drawn and Quarterly, 2014), 26. On graphic narrative and embodiment, see Hillary Chute,* Graphic Women: Life Narrative and Contemporary Comics *(New York: Columbia University Press, 2010), 193.*

capacious and potent medium for conveying a form of bodily experience that has proven stubbornly resistant to representation in other art forms, both visual and textual. It is by now a critical commonplace that the verbal arts struggle and often fail to capture the felt experience of physical suffering.[3] And yet, it is not the case that pictorial or visual art alone succeeds where words fail. Comics is an inherently hybrid form—one that is necessarily fragmentary and elliptical, that spatializes time and temporalizes space. Thanks to this very hybridity, it can hold steadily before the mind's eye a kind of human experience that all but eludes figuration.

This essay joins an ongoing conversation about the affordances of graphic narrative, a conversation recently energized by the rise of the graphic medicine movement. At the same time, it differs in both method and scope from most of the work done under the aegis of graphic medicine. Proponents of the movement most often seek to erase the clinical distinctions between the many facets of illness, to render a holistic portrait of disease as it is lived. In other words, the literature on graphic medicine tacitly accepts the increasingly prevalent—and, in many cases, very useful—biopsychosocial model of disease. It thus subsumes the sensory experience of pain into a broader aesthetic grammar of disease and disability. By contrast, in what follows I attend to a much more specific feature of comics as a visual and textual vocabulary—its strange capacity to render a form of sensation that can be neither said nor pictured.

Graphic Medicine and the Medical Humanities

The rise of graphic medicine may be traced to the birth of narrative medicine and, more broadly, of the field known as the medical humanities in the final decades of the twentieth century. The quiet success of these movements reflects a widespread concern among both patients and clinicians about gradual changes in the culture of American medicine during the postwar era. For Rita Charon, the founder of the narrative medicine movement, doctors' uninterrogated faith in ever-more sophisticated diagnostic technologies and therapeutic modalities all too often allows them to minimize the significance of the patient experience, including facets of illness and disability that no scanner or blood test can reveal. Charon argues that medicine, once an art of critical but empathic listening, has begun to abandon its commitment to the narratives constructed by patients about their own bodily experience, to treat subjective accounts of suffering with skepticism or outright hostility.[4]

---

3 *On the paucity of literary descriptions of physical pain, see Susannah B. Mintz,* Hurt and Pain: Literature and the Suffering Body *(London: Bloomsbury, 2014).*

4 *On the culture of postwar healthcare and the erosion of empathy in American medicine, see Rita Charon,* Narrative Medicine *(Oxford: Oxford University Press, 2006), 13–26.*

As Jared Gardner observes, the turn toward quantitative data collection and, above all, diagnostic imaging in healthcare has played a central role in this shift away from the broadly humanistic values and epistemological modesty that long characterized the practice of medicine. New forms of imaging—forms that would ultimately be reinscribed within the gestural, quivering, felt world by the hands of comics artists—promise to provide objective insights into the functioning of the human body:

> As the number of "objective" images proliferated and their resolution increased exponentially, it was inevitable that the weight accorded to those images would grow accordingly. Each of these technologies required specialists not only to operate but also to read them, specialists often cloistered away from contaminating patients' narratives.[5]

Narrative medicine represents a rejoinder to this unexamined faith in the glowing image—at its worst, a dangerous form of objectivist hubris that threatens to erode the doctor-patient relationship and to relegate the felt experience of illness to the margins of medical care. Proponents of the movement have established thriving curricula and even graduate programs in humanities departments and medical schools across the country. In their pedagogy and their scholarship, which borrow from the methods of literary and cultural studies, as well as aesthetics, philosophy, and sociology, they emphasize the centrality of storytelling and critical listening to the experience and understanding of both acute and chronic illness. Narrative becomes, then, a mode of therapeutic self-fashioning, a model for medical empathy and a diagnostic tool.

Graphic medicine might be understood as largely continuous with this project, a subfield within the larger movement of narrative medicine. The term "graphic medicine" was coined by Ian Williams, a doctor and cartoonist who has spent much of his career collaborating with scholars of comics, physicians, and cartoonists. These collaborators include Michael J. Green, a doctor who has integrated the study and even the making of comics into the medical-school curriculum at Penn State and has published numerous comics in medical journals, and MK Czerwiec, a cartoonist and hospice nurse based in Chicago whose work details her experiences on an HIV/AIDS ward. In 2015 this collective published *The Graphic Medicine Manifesto,* a collection of first-person reflections in both prose and comics on the intersection of graphic narrative and healthcare. As Gardner notes, the hybrid form of the work "puts to the test its authors' belief in the ability of comics to forge connections—between

---

5 *Jared Gardner, "Show Me Where It Hurts," Public Books, 15 Nov 2015, Web, n.p.*

medicine and the humanities, between doctors and patients—that prose alone often makes impossible."[6]

This understanding of the affordances of comics is by no means unfamiliar to historians of the form. As Scott McCloud has argued, the emergence of comics in the late nineteenth century reflected a much broader cultural shift toward visual-verbal hybridity, as artists began to explore the interactions between the two semantic systems. Comics are, by their very nature, at once elliptical and overdetermined; the form unfolds around the challenge of making meaning out of competing systems of signification, yielding a richer narrative than either alone could tell. [7] For the authors of the *Manifesto*, sustained engagement with this sort of multimodal text promises to return the medical profession to its founding humanism, ultimately dissolving the rigid oppositions between data and narrative, image and word, physician and patient, creator and reader. In other words, the hybrid nature of comics—a sophisticated interplay between word and image that unfolds in time—makes the form uniquely suitable to the depiction of illness as a complex form of lived experience rather than a series of diagnostic or therapeutic categories.

Both inside and outside the academy, the *Manifesto* was received with nearly unalloyed enthusiasm, even garnering significant attention in the popular press. For many of its readers, the turn to comics in the medical humanities stands as a rejoinder to the suspicion of lived experience in mainstream medicine.[8] This turn, however, is not altogether recent: scholars of comics have repeatedly emphasized that the history of the art form cannot be separated from the figuration of suffering, both mental and physical. "Illness," writes Gardner, "is arguably comics' invisible master theme, deeply woven into their genome and shaping the stories they tell, from the earliest newspaper strips (chronic allergies in Winsor McCay's *Little Sammy Sneeze*) through the rise of superhero comics (from Batman's PTSD in 1939 through the Fantastic Four's radiation poisoning in 1961)."[9] At the same time, the growing interest in autobiography among comics artists has created a new formal context for the graphic pathography, or illness narrative. For many cartoonists, the ur-text of this genre is Justin Green's *Binky Brown Meets the Holy Virgin Mary* (1972), which unfolds in the nightmarish psychological

---

6 *Gardner, "Show Me Where It Hurts," n.p.*

7 *Scott McCloud,* Understanding Comics: The Invisible Art, 2nd ed. *(New York: William Morrow, 1994), 193-215.*

8 *Abigail Zuger, rev. of* The Bad Doctor, *by Ian Williams, and* Graphic Medicine Manifesto, *by MK Czerwiec et al.,* New York Times, *30 June 2015, Web, n.p.*

9 *Gardner, "Show Me Where It Hurts," n.p..*

terrain of a patient with OCD.[10] By the mid 1990s, graphic illness narratives had begun to proliferate: Gardner cites, among others, Al Davison's *The Spiral Cage* (1990) and Harvey Pekar and Joyce Brabner's *Our Cancer Year* (1994). Indeed, according to a number of scholars, narratives about mental and physical illness have emerged as the "dominant form of nonfiction comics" in the twenty-first century.[11]

The Phenomenology of Pain and the Language of Suffering

And yet, even in the supple medium of comics, the felt experience of physical pain all too often seems to resist attempts at representation. Elaine Scarry's *The Body in Pain* helps us understand that resistance. Though it does not address graphic narrative, Scarry's work remains one of the richest phenomenological descriptions of pain. "Physical pain," she writes, "does not merely resist language but actively destroys it, bringing about an immediate reversion to a state anterior to language, to the sounds and cries a human being makes before language is learned."[12] For Scarry, pain represents the shattering of human language because it has no referential content, no intentional object. I hunger for food, dream of flowers, reflect on the events of the day, and yet I simply hurt. Pain, in other words, remains stubbornly and completely within the radius of the body, unanchored to anything outside of itself. It is at once utterly unverifiable and, for the sufferer, the most intimate form of truth, its facticity the very truth upon which all others depend:

> For the person in pain, so incontestably and unnegotiably present is it that "having pain" may come to be thought of as the most vibrant example of what it is to "have certainty," while for the other person it is so elusive that "hearing about pain" may exist as the primary model of what it is "to have doubt." Thus pain comes . . . into our midst as at once that which cannot be denied and that which cannot be confirmed."[13]

For Scarry, this disjunction—the seemingly unbridgeable distance between sufferer and witness—defines the experience of being in pain.

---

10 *On Green's aesthetic strategies and the history of the graphic pathography, see Hillary Chute, rev. of* Our Cancer Year, *by Harvey Pekar and Joyce Brabner,* Literature and Medicine 26.2 (2007): 414-415, and Hillary Chute, Graphic Women: Life Narrative and Contemporary Comics *(New York: Columbia University Press, 2010).*

11 *Gardner, "Show Me Where It Hurts," n.p.*

12 *Elaine Scarry,* The Body in Pain: The Making and Unmaking of the World *(Oxford, UK: Oxford University Press, 1987), 4.*

13 *Scarry,* The Body in Pain, *4.*

That distance erodes not merely the cognitive processes that subtend communication but the social promise of language—the human capacity to move out beyond the boundaries of the body and into a shareable world.

As critics have argued, this resistance to concretization in language may account for the surprising poverty of literary accounts of physical pain. Few novels, plays or poems present compelling portraits of the experience of migraine or neuralgia or end-stage pancreatic cancer. Most authors, all too aware of the limits of their own medium, carefully relegate the experience of the sufferer to the limits of the narrative frame. "English," writes Virginia Woolf, "which can express the thoughts of Hamlet and the tragedy of Lear has no words for the shiver or the headache ... The merest schoolgirl when she falls in love has Shakespeare or Keats to speak her mind for her, but let a sufferer try to describe a pain in the head to a doctor and language at once runs dry."[14] While true of the headache, Woolf's claim is, as Scarry argues, even more radically true of the severe and prolonged pain that may accompany cancer or phantom limb syndrome or tic douloureux.[15]

Scholars in literary studies, philosophy and narrative medicine, including Scarry, have nonetheless devoted considerable energy to studying attempts to render this helplessly private form of experience. Observers almost inevitably note that patients use two categories of metaphor to describe severe or chronic pain, either assigning it an agent—often a weapon—or imagining it in terms of visible (and therefore verifiable) tissue damage.[16] In the first case, sufferers speak of needles and nails and jackhammers; in the second, of burning and laceration. As Scarry argues, these two types of metaphor converge in that they assign shape, length, color or texture to the sentient experience of pain; in short, they externalize, objectify and make shareable forms of perception without any referential content.

This pressure toward embodiment or objectification pervades the figuration of pain in many graphic pathographies. In *Stitches* (2009), for instance, David Small recounts the physical pain and disfigurement he suffered after undergoing surgery for thyroid cancer as a child. Ironically, the cancer was likely caused by the misguided radiation treatments administered for a series of minor ailments by his overzealous radiologist father. The operation to remove his thyroid left him hurting and all but mute, his voice reduced to a barely audible rasp. Removing the dressing

---

14 *Virginia Woolf, "On Being Ill," in* Collected Essays, vol. 4 *(New York: Harcourt, 1967), 194.*

15 *Scarry,* The Body in Pain, *7.*

16 *Scarry,* The Body in Pain, *4-16.*

in front of the bathroom mirror, David confronts his surgical scar for the first time—the site of his pain, both physical and psychological:

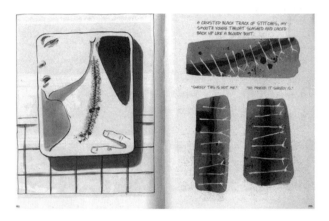

The full-page panel on the left depicts a moment of bodily identification and estrangement, David's sense that his skin is no longer wholly his own. The outline of the bathroom mirror becomes a panel-within-a-panel, a prison for the newly unrecognizable self. "Surely this isn't me," David protests. The body itself, suddenly personified, responds with cool cruelty: "No, friend, it surely is."[17]

Small draws the lunar terrain of his scar with an almost mannerist aesthetic of exaggeration, his neck thrust out at the reader. The gaps in the skin are rendered with a sublime attention to texture. On the right-hand page, Small zooms in on the surgical site, the lacerated skin, the individual threads—a "crusted black track of stitches"—tying his body together "like a bloodied boot." These panels thus reflect the difficulty of rendering the body in pain, the necessity of anchoring pain to externally visible sites of injury: the jagged skin itself becomes an objective verification of an otherwise invisible form of experience.

And yet pain, especially in its chronic forms, is often unaccompanied by any form of visible tissue damage. The rhetorical strategy of external objectification, however powerful, thus fails to capture the inherent blankness of pain with which I began, its lack of any referential or intentional object. In the absence of such an object, temporal markers take on a particular importance. Consider the adjectives frequently used by both patients and clinicians to differentiate various forms of neuropathic pain: "throbbing," "flickering," "pulsing," "beating," "shooting."[18] These

---

17 *David Small,* Stitches: A Memoir *(New York: W.W. Norton, 2009), 190-191.*

18 *Scarry,* The Body in Pain, *7.*

descriptions imply a temporal dimension, a rhythmic on-off sensation, presence followed by absence followed by presence. This register bestows on the experience of pain a sense of temporal extension that static metaphors fail to convey. One hears this very tempo in Emily Dickinson's account of pain, one of the most elliptical and yet intimately felt descriptions of physical suffering in verse:

> Pain – has an Element of Blank –
> It cannot recollect
> When it begun – Or if there were
> A time when it was not –
>
> It has no Future – but itself –
> Its Infinite contain
> Its Past – enlightened to perceive
> New Periods – Of Pain.[19]

Dickinson's characteristic ellipses here convey something of the inexpressibility of physical pain, its resistance to objectification in language. Pain eradicates the very sense of temporal continuity and extension that narrative requires; monolithic and unyielding, this infinite "It" reduces the sufferer's temporal horizon to a permanent, unchanging present. And yet the poem perdures, unfolding however tentatively in this reduced circumference, oscillating between the absolute presence—the sheer facticity—of pain and its maddening tendency to elude description.

This sort of oscillation imbues the perpetual present of pain with a palpable temporality. The effect depends largely on the formal features of poetry that emphasize the interplay of absence and presence: line breaks, the penumbra of white space around words and, in the case of Dickinson's poetry, the eloquent hesitancies of the dash. Hence the volleying of the lines between impossibly proximate antinomies: "Blank" and "recollect," "were" and "was not," "no Future" and "New Periods." For many poets, the challenge of conveying this sort of sustained prelinguistic experience remains the province of lyric poetry. Describing an excruciatingly painful flare-up of her rheumatoid arthritis, Adrienne Rich insists that poetry gives voice to forms of experience that other forms of verbal art cannot convey: "For that is one property of poetic language: to engage with states that themselves would deprive us of language and reduce us to passive sufferers." [20]

---

19 *Dickinson,* The Complete Poems, *323-24.*

20 *Adrienne Rich,* What Is Found There: Notebooks on Poetry and Politics *(New York: W.W. Norton, 2003), 48.*

The Hospital Suite: Drawing Pain

How might graphic narrative convey the temporality of pain without rei-
fying it? How might the medium allow artists to depict pain as dynamic
and temporal while bestowing on it an external and therefore shareable
reality? Here, the analogy with poetry proves apt. As Hillary Chute argues,
both art forms are invested in "extrasemantic visual rhythm," in conveying meaning through the disposition of space.[21] To better understand that
rhythm, we might turn to Scott McCloud's model of the internal dynamics
of comics in his seminal work of graphic criticism, *Understanding Comics*. Central to this model is the tension between the individual panel—a
self-contained visual and textual unit—and the sequence of panels that
make up a single page or an entire graphic narrative. For McCloud, much
of the aesthetic power of the form can be traced to the space between
panels, the so-called gutter: akin to the white space in poetry, the gutter
asks the reader to engage in an imaginative leap as she scans the page, to
connect the sharply delineated worlds of individual panels into a coherent narrative and aesthetic whole.[22] In this sense, comics demands of its
readers an unusual degree of participation in the creation of meaning.
One might even say that the reader assumes a subject position not wholly
dissimilar to that of the physician trying to piece together the inevitably
fragmentary, nonlinear account of a patient's symptoms into a coherent
clinical narrative. The artwork withholds as much as it reveals and, more
importantly, thematizes that very withholding, incessantly drawing our
attention to its own incompleteness.

Perhaps the most compelling account of this dialectic of presence
and absence comes not in a treatise on comics but in a work on
twentieth-century visual art. In "The Im/Pulse to See," Rosalind Krauss
defines postmodern visual culture as animated by a pulse, a rhythm that
constructs the Gestalt and at the same time undoes it, "positioning us
within the scene as its active viewer and outside it as its passive witness."[23]
Krauss argues that this beat works against the peculiar timelessness of the
modernist image, constantly dissolving the form it constructs; it thereby
relocates the aesthetic experience within the living body, "restoring to
the eye . . . the eye's condition as a bodily organ."[24]

This newly corporealized form of visual experience—immersive,
temporal, always on the brink of dissolution—describes the aesthetic

---

21 *Hillary Chute, "Secret Labor: Sketching the Connection Between Poetry and Comics,"
Poetry Foundation, 1 July 2013, Web, n.p.*

22 *McCloud,* Understanding Comics, *60-93.*

23 *Rosalind Krauss, "The Im/Pulse To See,"* Vision and Visuality, *ed. Hal Foster (New York:
The New Press, 1998), 59-60.*

24 *Krauss, 59-60.*

tempo of all graphic narrative, which constructs a self-contained world only to dissolve it. This tempo is all the more palpable in graphic pathography. Granted, Krauss's vaguely eroticized account of rhythm in the postmodern visual arts may seem distant from the figuration of pain in comics. And yet, this very dialectic allows comics artists to convey forms of somatic experience that would otherwise resist representation. Porcellino's *Hospital Suite*, for instance, records the author's descent into unbearable (and unexplained) abdominal pain. After many rounds of misdiagnosis, doctors find a benign tumor in his small intestine:

The top panel of this page gives voice, with striking economy, to a profound sense of the futility of modern medicine: though surrounded by the beeping of modern hospital machinery, Porcellino is doubled over, all but naked, his teeth gritted, his eyes closed. Despite the physical presence of his wife, Kera, he is ultimately alone. Lightning bolts of pain emanating from Porcellino's abdomen rupture the border of the panel, the very container of the narrative world. The reader then descends into the private hell of the bottom panel, where the world of the hospital—of doctors and painkillers and IV poles—suddenly disappears. The radius of narrative attention shrinks to the quivering contours of the human face. That face, streaked with sweat and dotted with stubble, is suspended in a void—a void that is nonetheless punctured by Kera's helpless murmur, muted by parentheses: "Can't you give him something for the pain?"

In these two panels, the contents of perception record the very process of perceiving. Though drawn from a third-person perspective, they body forth a rhythm of contraction followed by tentative expansion in which the narrative world is all but obliterated and then reconstituted in a fragile line, a single sentence: "Can't you give him something for the pain?" Pain may destroy language, but the language of others gradually recreates the world of the sufferer. *The Hospital Suite* oscillates again and again between immersion in the plenitude of the social and material world and devastating silences. After having his stomach pumped, Porcellino tries to detach himself from the immediacy of perceptual experience—the relentless onslaught of neural input—by reciting lines from the Heart Sutra, a founding text of Zen Buddhism:

Switching between a third- and first-person perspective, Porcellino depicts both the felt intensity of pain and his sudden sense of alienation from the sheer physical facticity of the surrounding world. The sweating, suffering face, depicted against a blank background, is utterly opposed to the menacing object world of the hospital lamp: the feeling, perceiving subject is completely divorced from the plenitude of the surrounding world.

These blinding circles of light embody the sense of utter alienation not only from the sterile facticity of the hospital room but from the very possibility of engagement with the social and material world. That world gradually dissolves into an empty panel:

The incantatory rhythm of the words all but eclipses the visible world of the narrative. This visual sequence reflects the narrowing of perception that pain entails; at the same time, it inscribes the felt experience of the sufferer within a recognizable object world. That very world reemerges as the fragile product of a perceptual process, of sentience itself:

Here, visual rhyme and verbal repetition convey the sense of an infinitely extensive present, in which the fact of sentience slows and all but stalls the forward motion of narrative: "It has no Future—but itself— / Its Infinite contain / Its Past." And yet in the bottom panel Porcellino does not simply choose to redraw the suffering face; instead, he opts for a more subtle aesthetic strategy, repetition with a difference. As a result, he creates in the reader the sense of spatialized time—an infinitely stretched moment that all but dissolves the punctual temporality of event.

Comics has a long history of depicting injury and physical pain, albeit in contexts far removed from the hospital corridor or the sickbed. In one of the earliest works in the genre, *Les Amours de M Vieuxbois* (1839) by Rodolphe Töpffer, the protagonist is repeatedly thwarted in love and in his many attempts at taking his own life. The superhero epic likewise features bodily damage that is most often miraculously undone in subsequent panels. More recent autobiographical works by Art Spiegelman and Alison Bechdel represent powerful challenges to this tradition, dwelling at length on the hurting body, though they are far removed from the genre of the graphic pathography.

And yet the sort of quiet lyricism that pervades graphic pathography represents largely uncharted territory for comics—a new mode of engagement with the medium itself, with its peculiar affordances. Porcellino's delicately drawn worlds are always on the verge of dissolving into a devastating blank, a blank anterior to language. Just as crucially, however, they reconstitute themselves again . ⁊

Works Cited/Consulted

Acocella, Marissa. *Cancer Vixen*. New York: Pantheon, 2009.

Charon, Rita. *Narrative Medicine*. Oxford: Oxford University Press, 2006.

Chute, Hillary. *Graphic Women: Life Narrative and Contemporary Comics*. New York: Columbia University Press, 2010.

— Rev. of *Our Cancer Year*, by Harvey Pekar and Joyce Brabner; *Janet and Me*, by Stan Mack; *Cancer Vixen*, by Marisa Acocella Marchetto; *Mom's Cancer*, by Brian Fies; *Blue Pills*, by Frederik Peeters; *Epileptic*, by David B.; *Black Hole*, by Charles Burns. Literature and Medicine, 26.2 (2007): 413-429.

— "Secret Labor: Sketching the Connection Between Poetry and Comics." *Poetry Foundation*. 1 July 2013. Web. 19 May 2016.

Czerwiec, MK et al. *The Graphic Medicine Manifesto*. University Park, PA: Pennsylvania State University Press, 2015.

Farinella, Matteo and Hana Roš. *Neurocomic*. London: Nobrow Press, 2014.

Gardner, Jared. "Show Me Where It Hurts." Public Books. 15 Nov 2015. Web. 2 May 2015.

Haines, Steve. *Pain is Really Strange*. Philadelphia: Singing Dragon, 2015.

Kleinman, Arthur. *The Illness Narratives: Suffering, Healing and the Human Condition*. New York: Basic Books, 1988.

Krauss, Rosalind. "The Im/Pulse to See." *Vision and Visuality: Discussions in Contemporary Culture. Vol. 2.* New York: The New Press, 1998. 51-75.

McCloud, Scott. *Understanding Comics: The Invisible Art. 2nd ed.* New York: William Morrow, 1994.

Porcellino, John. *The Hospital Suite*. Montreal: Drawn and Quarterly, 2014.

Scarry, Elaine. *The Body in Pain: The Making and Unmaking of the World.* Oxford, UK: Oxford University Press, 1987.

Small, David. *Stitches*. New York: Norton, 2009.

Zuger, Abigail. Rev. of *The Bad Doctor*, by Ian Williams, and *Graphic Medicine Manifesto*, by MK Czerwiec et al. *New York Times*. 30 June 2015. Web. 8 May 2016.

superstition [review]
an online literary magazine

[art, fiction, interviews, nonfiction, poetry]

Carmen Gimenez Smith
Colleen Abel
Gary L. McDowell
George Saunders
Kelle Groom
Major Jackson
Roxane Gay
Ruben Quesada
Sarah Vap

"I would recommend Superstition Review to anyone who wants good, honest writing."

The Review Review

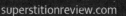

Libidonomics

Ross McMeekin

I was sold on Liz Fletcher well before we sat down for Mexican food. She checked groceries at the Smith's by my primary residence in the foothills and for the previous month I'd shopped there every day—sometimes twice—just to get a chance to talk to her. Let's say my aisles got stocked every time I saw her.

I'd asked her out a dozen times in jest until finally she said, *I'm off at five,* if nothing else just to shut me up. Understand: I'm neither young nor attractive. But I'm persistent and have money. A man has to make do with what he's got.

When our margaritas arrived, I asked her what she would do if she could do anything she wanted in the world and not worry about money. I told her that I didn't want to hear anything about world peace or planting trees for tomorrow. Those were fine, of course, but I wanted the secret desires, the selfish.

She blushed. "I've always wanted to be a model."

Of course she had. I imagine that by age ten, most women have spent thousands of hours walking down imaginary runways and across fictional stages with cameras flashing in adoration. But by God, here was someone whose childhood dream had a chance of coming true.

I asked her, "What's stopping you?"

"What do you mean?" she said.

She looked shocked that I'd taken her seriously, further proof of there being too many repressed snobs in the world making people feel bad for un-starched desires. Naturally, I asked her if she'd entered any beauty contests, gotten any photos taken, or queried any agencies. After all, this wasn't the moon. We were only a forty-five minute drive to downtown.

She shrugged and wiped sweat from the coupette glass with her finger. I'd shamed her. She was one of those beautiful girls who no one had ever taken seriously, someone folks assumed hid no depth, when in reality, she had hopes and dreams and feelings like everyone else. And here I was, pushing her to be something she'd never been allowed since she hit puberty: a normal human being.

As it would turn out, that conclusion wasn't just premature, but generous. I tend to imagine the best in people.

Anyhow, I apologized a couple of times until she made eye contact, and then asked her, dead serious, what kind of model she wanted to be—*c'mon, tell me*—and she took a long sip of margarita as if to once again bolster her confidence.

"Centerfold," she said. "Is that embarrassing?"

Her shoulder was bare and the light was proud to touch it. There is no shame in a nude human body, only glory. I wanted to make her dreams come true. I wanted her to never break eye contact with anyone again. "It's beautiful. Never be embarrassed by your dreams."

The waiter brought out an iron skillet full of beef and onion and pepper, still crackling and spitting. I worried our bare arms would get spot burns. Then and there, an epiphany blossomed.

"We can't eat yet," I said.

She nodded and folded her hands and bowed her head. She thought I meant we should pray first.

"No, darling," I said. "I've got something here. See, they bring out the fajita skillet too hot to eat, so that while we're waiting, we get that sweet experience of having our food in front of us, enticing our senses, but with an aching two-minute delay before it cools down to where we can dive in. We want it even more because we can't have it yet."

She blinked.

"Anticipation," I said. "Compels mothers to give up their firstborn."

She looked confused, and granted, what I said had no point of reference. I explained that I was talking about modeling and her dream of being a centerfold. We needed to find a way to make her too hot to touch. We needed to photograph her in such a way that the anticipation would be so thick and steamy her photograph would be irresistible to the powers that be.

"That's all we need to capture your dream," I said. And I began to improvise—while she nibbled at the beef—a loose plan to make her a star.

I got excited. I barely touched the fajita platter for the rest of the night. Her eyes were wide with what I took as awe.

Convincing Liz to quit her job and come live with me was more difficult than I expected, considering her alternate path of Vitamin D deficiency and tendonitis from spending her days as a checker at Smith's. Did I mention the medieval dump of a split-level she'd been living in with some outwardly morose waif from the meat department and a Chili's waitress with acne to spare? I offered her the car of her choice, a healthy allowance, a new wardrobe. She said it wasn't about that.

It started to make sense how Liz had gotten to where she was, both socio-economically and culturally. The world opens doors for beautiful women; by appearance, she should have been rush chair at her sorority, on the fast track to a cush PR job downtown, if not doing the weather for a network affiliate. Not sharing leftover pizza with the skee-ball team from the local arcade. I painted her as the humble victim. Desire is blind, but it won't just blind you; it'll make you see things that aren't there.

Liz said that living and working together might not be a good idea, and I thought she was being careful not to move too fast. I told her we'd have plenty of personal space—she could have the whole east wing of the estate and I'd never enter her territory unless she invited me over the intercom. My house is the largest in terms of square footage in the county, if you don't count sheds (and no one ever should, because hell, what's next, counting dog runs? Chicken coops?) You get the point: my house is incredible, and I say that for no other reason than to let you know that Liz's situation was, shall we say, improved.

Look, it's not like I needed her to be impressed, or even grateful. The last thing I wanted to invite into our relationship was more power dynamics than there already were, by virtue of our differences in age, beauty, and holdings. But it would have been nice if she at least recognized what I was doing for her, considering the lavish praise I gave for what she was bringing to the table (and, by the way, she ended up agreeing to take the allowance, car, and wardrobe, despite her misgivings).

Within the first week of our business meetings we decided our play would be to get her entered in the Country Cuties competition in one of the more reputable of the sensual magazines, *Steam*. The competition was open to the public. Contestants submitted pictures of themselves, and a panel of judges—combined with the online votes of users—winnowed the competition from semis to finalists to a champion. Winner got a cover, a spread, and an initial contract.

I did some market research and found that the track record of Country Cuties going on to modeling careers beyond that first contract was decent. Plus, I told Liz, since we were going the sensual route first, she wouldn't have to reveal the whole kit and caboodle. She'd get to make the rounds to the other sensual mags, do the swimsuit tour, and maybe even lock down a few films before showing it all. Naked didn't fit well with the fajita principle, at least not yet. The world hadn't even taken a bite.

Then I made my first mistake (other than the gracious assumptions regarding her character). It's funny how trouble always begins with virtue. I've always been proud of my discipline. I'm a routine guy, through and through. When *Forbes* did a web feature on my ethos—for anyone boring enough to care—I claimed discipline as the foundation of my success. So it was in my nature to believe scheduling each of Liz's days would help her become more productive.

I should also say that the schedule was absurdly laid back. Pandering, in hindsight. We'd wake up and shower separate, smoke a couple bowls and eat breakfast while watching *Good Morning America,* then work out in my fitness center. After that, she'd get free time for a few hours while I managed my fracking operations, after which we'd shower and meet up in the Jacuzzi and have a short little howdy neighbor before a light lunch. We only engaged in business in the afternoons, and even then, only until dinnertime. And most of that was research.

Sounds good, right? Liz hated it. She pouted from the moment I attached the schedule to the refrigerator. She thought I was trying to control her. *Lock her down* were the words she used. Then: *cage*. Cage! There were so many things I would have said if I didn't love her. That ninety-nine percent of the world would kill for such an imprisonment. That pride was the enemy of success until you'd achieved it. That if designer clothes didn't suit her, there was a vomit green apron waiting for her at Smith's on some rusted out hook next to the frozen Salisbury Steak *Hungry Man* meals that needed to be stocked.

I should have kicked her to the curb. Instead, I told her to remember the fajita. Remember the crackle! Remember your dream, my wildcat! You can do this. We can do this. "I know it's tough now, but it will all be worth it."

She took a deep breath, bit her painfully full lip, and finally relented. But consider the disagreement I just mentioned to be a foreshadowing of what was to come.

We stayed with this schedule for about a month with no real progress. We couldn't figure out how the fajita should look, and you only got to reveal a beauty like Liz Fletcher for the first time once. I wasn't about to have someone I was so dearly beginning to hate come off as trailer trash.

Then it came to me: the second epiphany. It was a Tuesday morning and already ninety in the shade, so we skipped the hot tub and instead took a quick ride in the shallow end of the pool, on an inflatable raft so Liz's backside wouldn't get scratched up just in case we wanted to do some pictures featuring her epic caboose. Then we relaxed and I went to the kitchen to get us iced tea and a joint from the humidor. When I came back out, Liz was still naked, but now in the middle of the pool on that same inflatable raft from our lunchtime screw.

And I saw it. Remember that old movie *The Graduate*? Northeast libs love that movie, and I knew for a fact that the ownership of *Steam* was littered with Delts from Dartmouth. So I imagined a way to play off the famous scene with the oh-so-young-and-existential Dustin Hoffman by dressing Liz in a classic sixties bra and panties and then posing her bored, reading a magazine, sexy as hell on a lawn chair—you guessed it—at the bottom of the pool.

It had the entire audience in mind. The simpletons would go for the skin, while the melancholies would get stiff from the subtext: *she was drowning and didn't even know it, like we all are.*

Well, once Liz realized I was serious about the shoot, she thought I was nuts. "How am I going to breathe?"

"We'll have a diver feeding you from an oxygen tank."

"That's not modeling," she said. "That's desperation."

I reminded her that quotidian definitions of beauty rarely captivated the hearts and minds of weary men. Take the *Seven Year Itch*, and how something as strange as Marilyn Monroe calling *delicious* the foul breeze from a Manhattan subway—up through an iron grate, billowing her dress, *oh here comes another one*—had aroused the complicated loins of generations. And when that wasn't enough, I reminded her of all that I'd done for her already and told her that if she didn't like it there was always a mop and aisle five (by that time I'd advanced in my weariness over her entitlement).

She agreed, but couldn't resist getting back at me for my little power play by informing me, that very night, over the intercom, that we would no longer be engaging in coitus, in order that she might better promote her sizzle.

Liz didn't warm up to *The Graduate* idea no matter how many times I tried to convince her. I'd learned by that point not to say anything, but I'd begun to question her resolve. It still never entered my mind that I might be getting played. I offered to get her coaches, dozens of them, for her posture, her gait, facial care, body toning, her diet . . . if she'd said the word she could have had a full staff of experts attending her every bowel movement. But she treated my suggestions—I only recognize this now, of course—how a prom queen from an 80s comedy might treat study skills advice from the hapless nerd who's going to end up doing her homework, regardless.

It's embarrassing to admit, but I'd become petrified of her leaving. I'd upped her allowance to the point that she was making six figures. She'd taken over driving my Maserati. No credit limit at Neiman Marcus. If she'd had the gall to ask me to sign over a stake in my mining empire, I might have agreed.

She developed, in the week leading up to the shoot, a glare that could freeze vodka. It both terrified me and made me feel more alive than I'd been in years. People wonder why the rich so often make such stupid personal decisions, seemingly at odds with their careful business management. It's because they so rarely ever feel fear, real fear, and when they finally do, it's like a drug. You always want what you can't have, but when you can have pretty much everything, each elusive jewel—no matter how stupid and toxic—becomes irresistible.

I neglected my business responsibilities to try and make it work. I hired a scuba instructor to hang out with her on the bottom of the pool, as well as an ocean photographer and an aquarium light specialist. They all looked and acted like young Harrison Fords: always getting away with something, always up to no good, but softies at heart. I perceived nothing. Her dream was all that I thought about. If I made her dreams come true, she'd be happy, then we'd be happy, and finally I would have a love that loved me back.

I'm convinced that all three of those hires slept with her, in my house—perhaps in my bed—and perhaps all at the same time! The evidence was there—swimsuits, body hair, stains—but I ignored them, like so many lonely men before me.

My team and I realized that while keeping the lawn chair situated on the bottom of the pool was easy, keeping Liz there wasn't. We'd failed to account for the fact that she had oxygen in her blood and lungs, desperate to bring her body back to the surface. One of the makeup artist's friends had dealt with this sort of thing before, so we flew him out from Los Angeles, too.

In the end, we didn't need the makeup artist's friend, because the solution was something a monkey could've figured out. We zip-tied the back of Liz's swimsuit to the lawn chair and got the photographs. And damned if they weren't hotter than a fajita from hell. Which is to say that hell is precisely as advertised: easy to dismiss but mighty difficult to resist.

Waiting for the results wasn't pleasant. I was so nervous I developed sores on the inside of my butt cheeks. I hadn't slept with Liz in over a month and she was skipping out on our Blue Dream parties, too, probably to spend my money snacking with big leaguers like the stallion of a first baseman I watched taking a piss in my Juliet rose grove one morning (I said nothing). I took her to buy some dresses from Herve L. Leroux in France. She moped. I took her to Beacher's Madhouse to rub elbows with Hollywood's finest. She spent the night in the arms of a beached reality television star.

That didn't matter to me.

I'd placed all my hope in her dream coming true and the situation at *Steam* was dire. The online votes got Liz into the semifinals, but our artistry was losing out to more blunt, carnal photographic invitations to the strong-wristed readership. A little encouragement was needed for tastemakers at *Steam*. I had my lawyer call them up and see if they required anything to help the process along, and sent over a bottle of Chivas Regal 50-year Royal Salute to each of them—along with boxes of Gurkha Black Dragons—to make my intentions clear. It was a loss, as a class gesture always is to those with negligible taste. My lawyer talked to a host of plebes who were offended that I would try to mess around with their stupid contest. Finally, after I called in a favor from a client with arms-dealer connections, we got someone on the phone with some fucking power. Now, you'd think the editor for a mid-level skin mag would exhibit a fair amount of moral flexibility. He balked. But he did say something helpful: "The only way she's getting on the cover is if you buy the damn magazine."

Call me a romantic, but if someone wanted me to make the cover so badly that they bought me a magazine to make it happen, I'd be pretty impressed. Maybe even touched.

Well, I took Liz out to dinner at the same restaurant we'd been in for the first epiphany to tell her the news.

"Liz," I told her, holding up a prickly pear margarita in a glass the size of a soup bowl. "Let's toast to you being not only the Country Cuties winner, but *Steam's* new cover girl."

I watched as the color drained from her cheeks and filled those deceitful lips to smiling.

My heart almost stopped. She hadn't smiled at me in months.

"Don't fuck with me," she said.

"We've got a conference call tomorrow with the new editor."

I'll be damned if a perfect little tear didn't form in each of her eyes, shaped just like Aphrodite's rear, and I'd be lying if a tear in the shape of the Hephaestus's stone heart didn't fall from mine.

"And Liz," I said. "It's only going up from here, because you're looking at the new owner of *Steam* magazine."

She was just about to give me a toast, but then stopped, glass mid-air, and a little of the margarita spilled onto the table in between us. "What?" she said.

"You can call me Mr. Publisher."

She set her margarita down. The tears dried up and a scowl wrecked her beautiful face. "So you're saying the only reason I won the contest is because you bought the magazine."

I tried to explain to her how this all works, how these contests, these magazines, these awards, none of them are fair; it's all business, all buying and selling and who wants something bad enough. Dollars make these things happen. I told her if it wasn't me, it would be someone else.

"This is proof of my love," I told her. Publishing? There isn't a worse investment. I was doing this for her. And hadn't her dream come true?

"You think you can buy me," she said.

"No, Liz, I'd never even think that, these are just gifts, this is how I show my love." I could have shown it in so many other ways—God knows I tried—but she wouldn't let me.

She yelled at me. Told me all of the things she'd probably been telling all of the other visitors at my place since I'd first invited her in. I'd destroyed her dream, apparently. She called me a dream hog, said she didn't ever want to model again, said she'd have been better off just staying at the grocery. "You can't buy Liz Fletcher."

The fajita plate arrived and there it sat in front of us, hot and sizzling, and we just stared until it went quiet.

She moved to Los Angeles with the boys. You've seen her, if you own a television or a computer. Can't help but see her, and deservedly so. But apparently I'm foul for recognizing it, and evil for helping her along.

Love someone, really love them. Try to make their dreams come true. Give everything. Save nothing for yourself. See what happens. ❧

On SWEET LAMB OF HEAVEN
(And Really All of Lydia Millet's Books)

Jessica Lee Richardson

I wrote my first ever fan letter to Lydia Millet after reading *How the Dead Dream*, *Oh Pure and Radiant Heart*, and then *My Happy Life* back to back in 2008 (wonderful books, all). Then the utterly unexpected happened. She wrote me back. She changed the course of my life by writing back. Among other kindnesses, she recommended I apply to the University of Alabama for an MFA. This was one of the best decisions I ever made, and it led to me meeting people I love and to me having a book out, too. After its publication I received a long letter from a fan, and of course, I wrote her back. A small extension of self can act on the world profoundly, I'd learned.

So I may be writing about Lydia Millet with some bias. But screw it, this is a recommendation, and I held that bias from her books before I ever internet-met her, or real-life met her years later on a college campus where after her talk attendees got high on a lavish slab of stone.

I just looked back on those early emails knowing I was going to write about Millet's new book, *Sweet Lamb of Heaven*. I expected some cringe factor, and it was there, but only in the recognition of my transparent desperation to be seen/not be seen by her, rather than in what I said about her writing. I just finished *Sweet Lamb of Heaven* and I stand by this assessment I made back then:

> I can't tell if its meaning is ultimately political — we are taught to docilely accept our lot in life no matter how insane and unjust it is, and we need to learn to stand up for ourselves — or — if its meaning is spiritual, acceptance leads to transcendence no matter where you find yourself, and we would do well to really notice the beauty and quit our whining. Or if it's a paradoxical combo, or neither. I like that I can't tell, therein lies the breathing . . . The poetry of your images and language have their own weight, beyond what their meaning is, that speak to the body and its dreaming the way a moral prescription couldn't ever.

I was talking about *My Happy Life*, but in some ways I could just as well have been talking about *Sweet Lamb of Heaven*, though they are very different books. Perhaps it's because I was being vague. I didn't have an MFA yet! But I think it's that Lydia Millet has a *thing*.

See? I'm not vague anymore. Cured.

Here is the thing, this was eight years ago. Since then Millet has authored a slew of new works, won a Guggenheim, and been a Pulitzer

Prize Finalist, but I am still shocked by how many avid readers I recommend her books to who don't know her work.

That odd obscurity may be changing with this latest book. I mean, *Vogue* reviewed it. There is a reason *Vogue* reviewed it. It's a compulsively readable page-turner. It's delicious. But Millet has not abandoned her experimental literary roots. She's just packaged them to be consumable. In a book that is in part about the sale of ideas, this entertaining, popcorn popping construct is form marrying content at its finest. It's that rare treasure that both entertains and engages the reader in a full throttle artistic encounter.

The story itself is simple, except of course it isn't. A woman escapes an emotionally abusive ex-husband and attempts to shield her daughter from him. A little backstory: the woman, who is not otherwise mentally different, heard voices for the first year of her daughter's life—a kind of stream of disparate but intelligent language that stopped when her daughter started speaking. Once the pair escape, the sociopathic husband, running for office and needing his family beside him as a campaign prop, seems to have almost superhuman abilities to track them and get into his ex-wife's head.

Written plainly like that, the plot seems almost absurd. It is one of Millet's much lauded gifts that she pulls off plots that seem like they may fall apart at any moment. Somehow they don't fall apart. Somehow in the end, they are not so absurd, or they are, but they are precise reflections of absurdities we are living. They are only casting colorful shading on a vision we have already accepted, so that we can see its lines. I mean, thematically, does the above plot description not sound a little like the experience of living in the cacophony of an ad-addled capitalist patriarchy?

Still, I thought hard about how Millet builds such trust on the story level while reading this book. (And there have been stranger premises than this in her books. In *Oh Pure and Radiant Heart*, famous nuclear physicists time travel and go on a road trip.) At one point I thought I was clever and had pinned it down. "Oh!" I raised my mental hand. "She makes the narrator as skeptical of events as we readers are to disarm us." But no. I recalled my fan letter-inspiring encounter with *My Happy Life*. That protagonist was the opposite. She took everything that came her way. She was an innocent.

When I got toward the end of *Sweet Lamb of Heaven* and I could feel with my hands that there were only about twenty pages left, I thought, oh, no. This is going to be another trilogy. There's no way she can resolve all of this!

But she did.

In fact the ending did that satisfying, fist to the heart, frozen axe, thinking about it for days, thing.

The best I can come up with on how she holds these plots together is that the tension lies in the why as much as the what. Her answers quiver with the honesty of her questions.

The lines I thought to include as illustrations are stunners, but I felt guilty plucking them from their contextual plumage fan. I'll drop this one here, though:

"True language is the deep magic. As old as time. God of the hills and water. God of the sun and trees."

The difficulty of excision is another of the book's gifts. It's full of aphorisms that *could* stand on their own, absolutely. See above. But they are cascaded toward contextually so that arriving on each tidbit of wisdom is an earned experience, a thrilling rise in the voice I learn to hear that is this book. It would cheapen these moments to pull them out of the wave of language they're riding. I will confess. I closed my eyes and actually said "thank you" several times at these rhythmic crests.

I suspect the reason it's hard to pin down Millet's craft is linked to this tight weave of language and effect. Also, how funny she is. How kind. To distill her choices into a cache of repeatable tricks would turn me into a kind of Ned of language. (Ned is the politician who's after our narrator.) Better to just let it be wild.

We eventually have to let go of all the tricks anyway, once we know of them.

In an era of emphasis on good literary citizenship, where writers themselves often float books in lieu of publishing muscle, I wanted to choose a good literary citizen to recommend here at *Post Road*. There are so many champions who deserve it! Instead I chose the book I had just naturally loved and it worked out perfectly. Lydia Millet works for the Center for Biological Diversity and writes powerful op-eds for the *New York Times* in defense of wolves, land masses, ecologies, and even, sometimes, humans. She is a good *actual* citizen. Who challenges us to put our tricks down and to stare directly at what is before us. Who also quietly writes back to gushing young women as if they, too, are literary. And then, poof, they are. Hers is that rare and beautiful art form that carries abstraction into the living, breathing world.

Magic. ❧

James Dean Posters on the Wall

Michael J. Hess

1.

Don't follow the sparrow too closely. I heard someone say that once. I don't remember who said it or where it was said or if it was said directly to me or if I heard it second hand or just overheard it. I do know I never took the advice. Just the other day, I followed a sparrow as it made its way down the Toronto shoreline. After it disappeared—sparrows always do—I discovered at my feet several pages that had been ripped from a book. The pages were damp and a dark slime created a Rorschach pattern on one side and there were even tiny bugs running up and down the edge, so I knew they had been lying on or near this spot for quite some time. I carefully picked up the pages between my finger and thumb like a diaper, shook them out (bye-bye bugs), and assessed my find. Turns out the pages were from *Final Exit* by Derek Humphry and they were from a chapter that was entitled "The Will To Die and Miracle Cures." Because adolescent boys and girls gather at this spot to smoke and drink and fuck, I thought this text might have been assigned as a project at their school. The boys and girls either did or did not do the assignment and then tore up at least a portion of the book. The sight of some pages flapping in the wind can bring smiles to the faces of all those rebels with or without causes. Who needs preachy books, anyway?

I made a trip to the Toronto Reference Library so I could peruse this book and this chapter. Curiosity. I'd never before heard of *Final Exit*. This particular book is stored in the stacks at the Toronto Reference Library and not on the shelves on one of the six floors, where anyone might retrieve and read it. One has to put in a stack request and wait—and wait and wait and wait—usually fifteen to thirty minutes, for a librarian to set it out on a metal cart or a shelf with your name on it. Hess, Michael. Handwritten in a fat pencil. Could it be a number one? Do people still use number one pencils?

The topic and content of the book is the reason that not just anyone can put their hands on it. The topic of the book is, generally, euthanasia. Many people buy this book, not because of the general topic, but because of the specific content: it instructs people on how to prepare and perform a successful suicide. I don't even like writing that last word. It too quickly plunges us into images and thoughts of isolates, the old and young alike, in contemplation and action. There are flashes of black there. The darkening of the frame.

So—*Final Exit* was probably not an assigned text in a high school classroom, which means that the book may have been used for its intended purpose, by someone interested in its advice on achieving an appropriate death through euthanasia.

"You ever heard of this book?" I asked my partner, Andrew. I produced the dirty pages from the shore.

He had come into contact with this book in a curious and morbid way in his younger years. An old boyfriend of his, Jim, had killed himself (is there a more subtle way to say it, and *should* I be more subtle?) using a modified technique from this book. Andrew knew he had followed the book's advice because he found a copy of it hidden among his belongings, the pages dog-eared and highlighted, studied. In the book Humphry advises a person who is ready to end his life to ingest a specified quantity of sleeping pills and alcohol, enough to make him fall asleep, but not so much that he will overdose. (There is an entire appendix of suggested drugs or drug combinations and doses in the back of the book.) After he takes the concoction titrated to the proper dose, the subject is told to wrap a plastic bag around his head and place a rubber band around the neck over the bag. The narcotics and the alcohol force the person to sleep and he peacefully suffocates. My partner said that Humphry used to suggest the subject sit with his fingers between the neck and the rubber-band-plastic-bag device until they would naturally fall away, but there was no mention of this step in the edition I read.

"You really know this book," I said.

"I do," he said.

My partner's boyfriend was a bit more dramatic in his approach: he used a rope on a cemetery tree instead of a rubber band in an easy chair to achieve his end, but the effect of the plastic bag and the sedatives was the same. He even tied the rope on the tree in such a way that he was forced to stand on his tippy toes, so that if he didn't suffocate by plastic bag—if Humphry's technique somehow failed—he would have hanged, and died by strangulation.

Andrew read through the book, Jim's book, which was technically now Andrew's—possessions shift hands after exits—shortly after the suicide. Andrew never saw that book in Jim's grip while he was alive. If he had, he might have considered there was something really "going on" with Jim—a clue. You see, Andrew was still looking for some sign or red flag that he might have missed, still wondering if there was something he could have said or done to have prevented the final act that occurred on that cold November day. Journals with plots, email correspondence, notes in the margins of *Final Exit*: it was all there once he knew to look for it. Dark things, angry things. Andrew read through all this material, read through enough of it anyway, and then he deleted the emails and threw all the hard items into the fireplace, incinerated them. No one needed to read the words of a young man who had followed instructions so closely, who had so abruptly taken flight from this mortal plane.

2.

Immortality, it might be said, is not so easy to earn. A young person who loses his life at the height of his youth—of his "powers"—might be said to attain some form of immortality. The catch here (the one fly in the ointment, the reason more aren't lulled into the dying-young narrative) is that you had to have done something or represented something, or both, in order to achieve this reverence, preferably in our culture attained cult status as a singer or an actor or a poet. James Dean was a boy who did just that. He was a boy from a small farm town in Indiana who moved to California and then New York and then California again, a boy who drank milk and raced cars, a boy who liked speed, a boy who might or might not have had a death wish, who might or might not have been conscious of that death wish if he in fact had one, and who became famous as a method actor and as a symbol of tormented youth and who, at the height of his fame (there were only three movies, *East of Eden, Rebel Without a Cause,* and *Giant*), crashed his Porsche Spyder into a Ford Sedan on Route 466 in Cholame on September 30, 1955. This car crash was or was not a suicide, but after the release of *Rebel Without a Cause* four days later, it was read as one in certain circles.

There is no way to know what, if anything, was going on in the head of James Dean when he crashed his car on that California highway, just as there is no way to know what was going on in the head of Jim when he walked into that cemetery with the plastic bag and the rope. How do we get into the mind, or headspace, of a young man who has just committed or potentially committed a final act? Short answer: we don't. What we try to do is go into our own heads, search through that vast and mysterious labyrinth: imagine (or re-imagine, as the case may be) ourselves wanting to end our own lives. This is tricky business because it is based on the assumption, always wrong, that we could actually project in our mind's eye what is looping in the mind of another. Even when we live with someone, share a bed and dreams and dares, endure bad habits, bad breath, we cannot crawl into that other's sacred headspace. We just can't do it, no matter how hard we may try. This means, flatly, that we have to be prepared for our nearest and dearest turning into rogue agents ready to pull off hara-kiri—at any moment—without our knowledge.

In *James Dean: Mutant King,* a tabloid biography by Dan Dalton, there is a picture on page 338 that shows Dean jumping off the roof of a building. The picture looks like it might be a film still from *Rebel* or *East of Eden* or *Giant.* The book lacks captions or a picture index and I'm too lazy to scour these films in search of the particular frame for proof. Whatever the context, James Dean has inscribed this picture with the words: "Try to catch me. You think I have to come down from up here, don't you. I hate all earthlings. Love, Jimmy." The address, *earthlings*—did Dean see himself in certain ways above the human fray? In some sort of rarified air? Others certainly saw him this way. The words are written on *that* picture, where he's jumping. Suicides sometimes jump. Did he have a wish to end his life, conscious or not? Did he know he'd be taking his final flight so soon?

3.

Humphry distinguishes between passive or active euthanasia. Passive euthanasia is when the doctor can legally "pull the plug" to stop providing life giving services so the patient might die. Active euthanasia is the deliberate plan, or plot, to end one's life because one is in severe pain, or otherwise deteriorating (Alzheimer's, Parkinson's, certain cancers), or about to deteriorate. It is this active suicide that is the focus and controversy of *Final Exit.* Humphry implores his readers who might one day want or need to implement this type of final release: "Why not have a trial run? So long as you are fit and alert, you can take the bag off easily." But when Humphry points out that Don Shaw from Chicago tested out this method by himself, and when he points out that Shaw then demonstrated the method to a local Hemlock group, then points out that Shaw said, "Everyone was both amused and impressed," and "I urged them to go home and try it on for themselves in order to get more comfortable with the whole concept," I had to question whether any person should become comfortable with such a serious act. Demonstration too easily blurs into theatre, and should individual initiated suicide ever move into that arena?

When Jim died, this was the theatre. There were police officers and newspaper reporters at the cemetery who all needed to get the facts of the story down. Imagine red flashing lights and open reporting pads and "take all the time you need." There were statements—"easy, easy"—that were provided by my partner and the people who knew Jim who had gathered there. And people had gathered there: word of suicide, especially of a young man in a public cemetery—which brings up the sensational topics of cult sacrifice and Satanism—spreads as fast as brushfires out West. There were some people who could not talk that night, but who would talk later. There were people who would never speak. "Take me to the electric chair if you have to!" No one who did speak that night remembers exactly what he said. Can they really use the testimony of witnesses who've just experienced a cosmic shock? These are people who would be imagining Jim's death by imagining their own. They are people who would be too close to the precious coil to provide any lucid remarks.

After the car crash in Cholame, California, that took James Dean's life, another type of theatre commenced—the cult worship of a revered, and now deceased, star. The James Dean Death Club and the James Dean Memory Ring and the James Dean Foundation in Indiana, among others, were quickly established to handle the public's appetite for the lost star, real places to send correspondence, buy memorabilia, engage in community discussion and mourning. This was before the Internet, remember—before digital networking, before we could easily connect and share our thoughts and feelings with a group of like-minded others all at once. Letters, some fifty thousand, were written by fans and addressed to Warner Brothers Studios from places all over the globe, so the studio "had to hire two independent companies just to handle the deluge." People *needed* Jimmy. Fans paid fifty cents to sit behind the wheel of the crashed Spyder, to sit in the seat he sat in, "impregnate them with his essence." There were national and local James Dean look-alike contests: "In 1956, a Pennsylvania high school student received some twenty-thousand letters acknowledging him as the Official James Dean Look-Alike." At one point every young person in every high school in America was trying to look like Dean—red jackets everywhere, like poppies in an open field.

There were public and personal ceremonies. Jim Bridges, a director and screenwriter, would recount, ". . . we all went to a place called the Polaram and bought lots of booze and got really plastered. We just couldn't stand it. We went down to the river and built a fire and had our own wake. Then we had a mud fight and started chanting, 'Give us a sign, give us a sign,' and we all had our shirts off. A dog barked on the side of the hill, so then we knew he was there . . . ." Many thought his body was gone, but his spirit very much alive, more than alive—he was a ghost walking among the crowds interacting in invisible ways. One magazine played to this magical idea, *James Dean Returns!* READ HIS OWN WORDS FROM BEYOND THE GRAVE. His words from beyond the grave told of "How I found a new life beyond death through one girl's love . . . ." The grave, it seems, is not a fine place for a man who would be (mutant) king.

4.

Jim worked full-time as an employee for the telephone company and he was someone who lived with chronic pain. His pain centered around his jaw line, a facial ache that radiated throughout his head, neck and upper body. He couldn't sleep or eat or kiss on certain nights, which made him look tired, run down. Sex, especially oral, was unpleasant. A cock in the mouth was like a knife in the back of the throat on certain nights. But the pain wasn't always peaked—a ten plus, say. There were times when the sensation was more of a dull throb, meddling, a fine agitation to the nerves, like that of an impacted and irritated tooth in the dead of night.

I project what his pain was like here. I do, dear readers. When we talk about another's pain (or even our own), this is always the way it has to be. There's really no way to know. We ask the sufferer to register the pain on a scale of one to ten, but there's an inherent gap in our understanding:

we don't know if your ten is the sufferer's ten. There are other tests that help us more closely approximate the severity of the pain—the Visual Analogue Scale, the Brief Pain Inventory—but even with those tools we still only attempt to approximate a sensation. To this point, there very well may be pain that is too acute for some people to endure, and if you haven't experienced it (although there would be no way to verify if you had experienced it or not) you just don't know. *So fuck off.*

These patients can be considered "difficult" and difficult to treat. Many doctors prescribe them drugs, mainly opiates, because it quickly reduces at least some of the symptoms of the pain, and importantly, shuts them up. Unfortunately, the effects of the opiates soon wear off and the dosages need to be increased to provide even a modicum of relief. This leaves the individual hooked on the prescription drug, even though it is losing and will continue to lose its effectiveness through time. Jim was a person who was prescribed drugs for his jaw pain that were losing their effectiveness through time. Jim was frustrated. He wanted relief from the symptoms.

"Jim was never properly diagnosed," Andrew would offer.

Andrew would know, too. Andrew was a young neurologist. Jim turned to him in his time of need (all times were his time of need, according to Andrew) to help him sort through his jaw-pain issues. *There must be some sort of relief. Can't I get down to a one or two, at least?* Andrew spoke to him about what might be going on, printed out the relevant medical literature, booked him in to see a specialist or two. But Andrew could take a hard line in his involvement in the treatment of a loved one. That's the way he was trained and wired.

"I'm not your doctor," I can hear Andrew saying.

"So you can't help me?" I can hear Jim saying.

I know this conversation because I've had similar ones with Andrew many times over the years. Like walking up to a window at the social security administration and being denied a benefit because you forgot to sign your name on a line, a partner of Andrew's can feel a real bureaucratic edge. Andrew doesn't like to mix up his medical practice with his personal relationships. Even when he speaks to his elderly parents, who are having health issues:

"Go talk to your doctor," Andrew says.

"But I'm talking to you," his parents say.

"Only your doctor can—"

Even when Andrew is talking to his younger brother *about* his parents.

"We just wanted you to translate some of the Latin," his brother says.

"Have them ask the doctor to clarify. Go to other health care professionals, the library." *Don't ask me.*

Andrew's brother was finding out what Andrew's parents were

finding out, what Jim had certainly found out, what I knew: Andrew can be a real prick when asked to come to the family table with his professional toolkit. Should we speak to Andrew as if he is not a doctor? Should he abandon his skills, pretend he doesn't have information that might be helpful? Of course not. We, the family members, just have to learn not to push too hard for medical advice, and when Andrew grows agitated dispensing his wisdom, to pull back. We further have to learn to not always turn to him during those times when we might most need his reassurance and support. The question is: How did this dynamic play out in this early relationship with Jim?

Andrew thought that Jim's pain—like most pain—was both physical and psychological. As I've alluded to, there was some sort of repetitive sexual abuse at the hands of his older brother—a forced blow-job every now and then from the bloodline. This would help explain why the pain in the jaw was so severe and would flare up during highly emotional and stressful situations. Jim was also brought up by a mother who adhered to a rigid interpretation of the Bible. She seemed certain that God hated homosexuals based on some whacked-out line in Leviticus. She believed the homosexual was destined to burn in hell for all eternity, and if Jim was really a homosexual, her reasoning went, he, too, would burn in that fiery pit. She needed him not to burn. She was a woman who *could* get her mind around the red tape involved in obtaining an everlasting life.

James Dean was a rumored bisexual or homosexual. Did he repent at any point before the crash? Or is he consumed in eternal flames right now? Or, is scripture as a mouthpiece for eternity a bit more elastic than its interpreters would have us believe?

5.

Rubber bands can stretch and rubber bands can snap. That day Don Shaw demonstrated affixing a plastic bag with a rubber band to his head to the local Hemlock group, he would discover the rubber band was much easier to put on the bag before it went over the head "like a hat," and that "two average rubber bands were adequate." I have to question the findings of Mr. Shaw, documented by Humphry, here: could an average rubber band really "easily" fit around someone's head? I use rubber bands fairly regularly to hold together stacks of papers or groupings of pens or hair, and they have a tendency to snap. The rubber loses its elasticity almost from the start. Age tends to harden it. Add to this the fact that human heads can be large in size or deformed or even macrocephalic and finding a durable elastic product for active euthanasia could be quite a challenge. Perhaps when Mr. Shaw mentions two rubber bands, he is thinking of them tied together in knots to make a super rubber band for a super release? Why do I focus on a little piece of rubber with no beginning or end?

When I was a child, my brother wrapped a rubber band around his wrist very tightly to see what would happen. He wrapped the rubber band so tightly that he was unable to take it off and his hand quickly turned purple. He had to run inside and have my mother cut it off with a pair of orange sewing scissors. Rubber bands can stop the flow of blood to those parts of the body that are most distal. They can be difficult to get off on your own. Should we be warning our children of the dangers of rubber bands? They can even be lethal, when they work.

I had to imagine what would have happened if my mother had not been around on that day. Two kids: would we have found the orange sewing scissors in the junk drawer? If not, would I have, in survivalist fashion, placed my teeth on the band near the bulge of his hand, and severed it with my central incisors? Or would we have let the hand go?

I think about that hand quite a bit. I see it disembodied from my brother. I see it as a lifeless extension sitting under a piece of museum glass. People come by to view it, gawk, to see what comes to those who play with those simple bands of rubber. I see it the color of a bruise. I see it more at certain times than others. I see it and am always reminded of how quickly the supply can be cut off.

6.

Andrew would describe a night a month before they found Jim hanging from a tree in the cemetery. It was a cold October night in Volunteer Park in Seattle. This was a popular cruising ground for gay men of all ages. Andrew stopped by after a grueling day of work, around 7:30 PM. He would have been a resident at the University of Washington, a pediatric neurologist on call five nights a week. Jim was there, too, hunting for something that might dull or explain the pain. The relationship between Andrew and Jim was moving toward separation, so certain freedoms had been granted, if not fully acknowledged. Andrew passed by Jim that night in the park. They passed each other near a street lamp so the faces of each were fully exposed. Andrew said that Jim looked pale and white. White white. Andrew would refer to that night often, to the ghost who passed before him and then vanished into the mist, only to be self-delivered into history one month later.

I remember when Andrew told this story that he said that he was being followed for sexual purposes and that Jim was not. The idea was this: if he stopped and talked to Jim, he was going to lose this chance. Yes, there were millions like this, but it was cold and he didn't want to stay out there all night, didn't want to troll, and *Jesus Christ, we aren't really together anymore,* and this chance was important right now because it conferred on the subject the one thing he wanted more than anything else in the whole world—to feel his animated self mashed up with another so he could feel really alive, or just imagine himself so.

There was a good chance that Jim didn't go out there that night to participate in playground shenanigans, but to wander around like a ghost in a Dickens tale, in order to receive a message or lesson or clue that might confirm or refute the sentence handed him by the strange agencies within and without. How many of us have had confrontations with those others who were on that strange border between this life and the next? Those stark encounters that forgo all forms of communication, save the basest of them all, the one we used even before we knew we were using it: the ability to gaze on the face before us in wonder. Maybe this is why we love the movies—life-sized faces that subsume us in those darkened rooms. James Dean, according to Dalton, had "a face of American bedrock, as pure and strong as a block of Carrara marble, and from this matrix he shaped himself." And us.

The idea that there was some sexual competition that night, that Andrew was getting more than Jim was getting, is something to explore. I bring it up because there was a motive for Andrew not to really speak to Jim on that night, a motive "not to get into it." A person who has lost a loved one to suicide often beats himself up for the past behaviors and actions that may be perceived to have pushed the other over the edge. In Andrew's head, is this the story he tells himself, that *I didn't want to talk to Jim that night because it was more important to turn a trick?* And if he hadn't turned the trick or tricks, would Jim not have taken the pills and tied the rope and stood on his tippy toes? The stories we tell ourselves in order to live are the stories we tell ourselves about others—and frequently, about that one other who spins our life into butter with their crazy, and sometimes loving, antics. This certainly is not Andrew's fault. But is it any wonder that after leaving the medical profession and then re-entering it that he would change his focus from that of a child neurologist to that of a specialist in pain and addiction? Do we all think of ourselves as the puppet master who is able to resurrect the lost souls wandering around in our kingdoms?

7.

Pinocchio is the story of a puppet master named Geppetto who eventually turns a wooden boy into a real one. I used a shot from the animated *Pinocchio* by Disney for a video exercise for *Sight and Sound I* during my first summer at film school at New York University. At nineteen, I was a very centered student, one who got his work done on time, performed well enough on the outside, achieved remarkably high grade points (points which really had no point), but one who had not resolved, or even really understood, his family past, or himself. The video piece I composed was basically a bare monologue of myself revealing all the gory emotional details of my family life. Throughout the exercise, I slowly and dramatically moved out from a wide shot and into an extreme close-up. No subtleties here.

I remember herding my classmates into a small room to watch this piece, the Beta machine ticking away the frames of this amateur one-man confessional, while I stood outside, alone. There was toward the end of this piece, if I recall correctly, the idea of transformation—of understanding and then rising above my past. To rise above it, I believed back then, it was necessary to separate myself from my family, the tribe, to implement a radical cut. That meant I needed to stop talking to my mother and father, my grandmother and grandfather, my aunt. I needed to spend holidays with friends or other families or eating Chinese and Japanese on Canal Street. I needed to stop mentioning my past in conversations, needed to focus only on the always promising or fraught future. Futures are always thought of in drastic terms. This was a dangerous point in my life. I was not suicidal, far from it, but my view of myself and the world around me became distorted and heavy, myopic. I had cut the strings that had, however poorly, held me up, severing the life source and force that had been feeding me my best moves and lines. What was guiding me now?

Things can go terribly wrong for certain individuals here. They cannot negotiate the choppy mental waters as they try to sort through the people and ideas of the past and the promises and predations of the present. Not every person comes through this. Even those of us who do come through don't come through Downy clean. We're absolutely marked and wrecked, chicks taken from the nest too soon, forced to mature before we are really ready to do so. Becoming ourselves—our true ungodly selves—is the most tortuous process of all, and the most important. The shot of the *Pinocchio* film I used to represent this transformation was the moment when Geppetto brings Pinocchio to life, when the animation of the animation—the miracle—occurs and the puppet becomes a real boy.

There may be no miracles in life, but there are real actions that can produce cosmic effects. The video instructor for that *Sight and Sound I* class wrote me a letter a month or two after that class. A few lines pop out: "Feeling alienated from oneself is very unpleasant. And sometimes it takes a long time to set that aright. I hope you won't be too impatient about that." These are good words. Every lost boy should hear them at a particular point. That some boys may not be able to hear these words even if they are spoken or written is a conundrum that I can hardly confront. Why can some fold these messages into the interior and move on, while others remain trapped in an uncompromising loop? Why Jim? Why Jimmy? Why them all?

8.

"I think there's only one true form of greatness for man. If a man can bridge the gap between life and death. I mean if he can live on after he's died, then maybe he was a great man . . . to me the only success, the only greatness, is immortality." James Dean supposedly said that. I went to the library to check the accuracy of my quote. The Internet is dangerous with facts. I opened *James Dean: The Mutant King* only to discover in the upper left-hand corner on the inside cover a small sticker. Black lines of varying widths: a barcode. I realized that every library book now comes with one of these stickers. Books used to come with an index card that slipped into a pocket in the back of the book. A library user would hand write her name on a line on the card and the librarian would stamp it with a date. The user would have two weeks from the checkout to return the book, one renewal if necessary.

I bring up the cards because they allowed any person who picked up the book the ability to see who checked out the book in the past. All one had to do was pull out the card and read the list of names. I could not see who read *Final Exit* at the Toronto Reference Library. Cards in the backs of library books are a thing of the past. All information is now stored on a central computer server. Our names are there.

9.

Andrew said that Jim hanged himself in the cemetery where Bruce Lee is buried on the day of his own death, which he related as a suicide. Andrew got his facts wrong. The official story is that Lee did not try to kill himself. This was rumor. (James Dean's suicide is rumor, too.) Lee died of cerebral edema at the age of thirty-two, possibly from a drug interaction (analgesics, muscle relaxants, and marijuana were implicated but never proven; "death by misadventure" was the line the doctors took) on his way to Queen Elizabeth Hospital on July 20, 1973. Further, Jim's suicide coincided with Lee's birth, not his death. The mix up of the facts gives one a clue as to the headspace that Andrew was in after the event, and perhaps still is.

Andrew was certain that Jim would have been aware of the details of the events of Lee's life. He would have planned his self-deliverance to coincide with dates and locations that were significant in that regard. And isn't it in the details where we all give ourselves away? I then thought of how popular culture anoints its Gods. You had to have done something or represented something—be a famous singer or actor or poet. This is the requirement of our age, of our ages. This is probably why Jim performed the act on the same day that Bruce Lee was born in the cemetery where he was buried. History won't remember a person who was not famous, won't remember an employee from the phone company who felt indescribable facial pain and the effects of abuse and God's judgment and a ruptured family line. But he might be remembered by association, by a terrifying self-deliverance that coincided with someone else's deliverance. Be immortal. Catch me if you can.

10.

Under a glass case, in a distant corner of my mind, a purple hand twitches.

11.

Andrew and I drove out West last summer and I finally had a chance to walk through the cemetery in Seattle where Bruce Lee is buried and where Jim ended his life. It was a hot day with a flat sky that was somewhere between blue and gray—hazy and bright at the same time, all wrong. The grasses were scorched because the city hadn't been getting enough rain and the grounds keepers must not have seen the point in setting out sprinklers to keep the grasses green. The brown grass made the red, white, and blue flags and the carnations and roses and windmills stand out, colorful relief in a land of repose. There were no birds out that day, no song.

The cemetery was surrounded on all sides by a cyclone fence. It was tall but could be easily mounted and climbed over, if one wanted to get in when the gates were locked. Jim must have climbed over the fence on that night in late November, the tips of his shoes poking into the diamond links. Every person who is reading this has climbed over a cyclone fence at least once. We all know how to do it. It's easy enough.

Andrew and I walked up the main path for a bit and then veered into a row, walked between some graves of varying shapes and sizes. We came to a couple of trees, elms. They grow well out here. Andrew told me so. Andrew circled around them, studied them, like a bug expert assessing a beetle infestation. All he needed was a brimmed hat with netting and a notebook.

"This is it," he said. He put his hand on the trunk of the tree he was in front of.

We walked around some more.

"I'm *pretty* sure it was that one," Andrew said.

We came to another tree. Andrew again walked around it, looked up at its long heavy branches. His hand touched the rough bark.

"Maybe this one," he said.

There were a couple more trees that it could have been.

12.

A friend stayed with Andrew the night after the morning they found Jim. Andrew tells me that the friend brought over a bottle of bourbon and they drank heavily. It was a cold November night in Seattle, just after Thanksgiving. The bourbon warmed the body the way a fire warms a room. Andrew would repeat to me how cold it was that night. Cold, cold. Andrew doesn't remember much more about that night. He remembers the call to his own parents and he remembers the call to Jim's parents, but he doesn't remember what was said, the content of the conversation lost like a warm mitten on an icy trail. He doesn't remember if he ate or not, probably not, but he can't be sure. His friend slept on the pullout couch. Andrew slept in *their* bed.

"Was that hard?" I asked.

No answer.

13.

I am reminded in the Toronto Reference Library that day thinking it absurd that *Final Exit* was stored in the stacks. I thought that with the revolution of the Internet that the content of this book could easily be gleaned from a Google search or posting on a blog or individual websites. Surely, there is information here that is more incendiary, more provocative, and perhaps less accurate in its instructions. But the event that Andrew endured did give me pause and made me consider how we pass along or restrict information. There may be people who are just one sentence or paragraph or chapter away from committing to a final act.

One other thing I remember from that day at the Toronto Reference Library. A sparrow was inside the library. It was flying around and landing on various surfaces. The bird did not land on the tables where individuals and groups were studying, but on the floor, in the potted plants, the windowsills, and on the tops of the bookcases. I remember no one paid the sparrow any mind, but I tracked its movements. I always do.

The sparrow that day brought to mind the gospel song, "His Eye Is on the Sparrow." I have an album by Della Reese who provides a rendering of this song that is, according to the back cover, "a gasser." I also have a VHS tape somewhere in our basement of a young black boy singing this song. He spontaneously stood up one day in one of my classes and asked if he could. Why not? When he opened his mouth, out came this beautiful spiritual. He sang it a cappella. Everyone was very moved by his interpretation and performance and gave him a standing ovation from their little desks. I must have recorded it for some point in the future. This moment is that point in the future. And, still, I don't know why I recorded it, or for whom. I do know there are no lyrics to the sparrow's song, but its music is remarkably sweet. ❧

Herrenvolk

Timothy Scott

With her blue eyes, Oxford shoes, and the pink ribbons she wore in her hair, Ludwicka Kuplicki, or L.K. as we came to call her, looked like one of the illustrations in our reading textbook, *Broad Horizons*, and Hughey had his eye on her from the moment she arrived in our seventh grade classroom at St. Paul's. He liked his girls white and blond. Unlike those girls, though, L.K. wasn't impish or animated. She'd come to Detroit from Poland, and barely spoke English. Our homeroom teacher, Mrs. Crenshaw, didn't seem too thrilled about having another student dumped on her in the middle of the year, especially one she had to repeat everything twice to. She was strict, wore dashikis and super long, press-on nails, and had once gotten in trouble for refusing to lead our class in the Pledge of Allegiance. Since all the desks had been taken, she put L.K. at the end of a long table where the Habitrail and aquarium sat. In class, she never made eye contact, and when called on, looked so nervous that it made everyone uncomfortable, and teachers gave up. At recess, she'd sit by herself against the rectory wall, reading a book. After school, her father would be waiting in a brown Cutlass and whisk her home. Hughey tried to chat her up a few times, to "lay his rap" on her, but she'd just shake her head and walk away. I think she was afraid of him.

Hughey and I had been friends since second grade. We had birthdays that were just two days apart (June 10th and 12th), had scored the same composite (97) three times on our SRAs, and both had older brothers who'd died (Hughey's in Vietnam when we were in first grade, mine of spinal meningitis the following year). Our similarities, though, ended there. Hughey was black, me, white. He was on the tall side, and very muscular, while I was short, with chipmunk cheeks and a roll of baby fat that hung over the clasp on my corduroys. Outside of school, he wore silk shirts and tight tank tops, while I stubbornly stuck with cartoon character t-shirts I'd ordered from a cereal box. He was outgoing and fearless; I was shy and trouble-averse.

My initial reaction to most of Hughey's schemes was to beg off. "Let's take my dad's car for a drive downtown," he said once, when his parents went out of town. "I should get home," I said. "I have to feed Napoleon." (Napoleon was my salamander. I fed him flies that I'd catch in my hand, then dash against the pavement). "Really, Russell? Really?" Hughey would say. Then he'd wheedle, cajole, and humiliate me, until he got his way, and we'd do something like take a two-hour joyride in his dad's gold Lincoln, cruising down Woodward past strip joints and party stores, stopping at Pelzer's for a bag of Funyuns and an Orange Crush, before docking the battleship back in the garage—it was tricky, too, you had to stop the moment the front windshield hit the tennis ball on a string, or it wouldn't fit, but Hughey did it. We were eleven years old.

At St. Paul's, the nuns had it in for Hughey, and vice versa. In third grade, when he got into a fight with Doug Dozier, a fifth grader, Sr. Annalise pulled him off him by his Afro, ripping out a chunk, leaving a divot on his scalp. Hughey never forgot it, and two years later, walking by her empty classroom, he looked around, popped in, and took a leak into her coffee pot. At recess, we watched through her ground floor window as she took a sip of coffee, grimaced, and spat it out in the sink. We dined on the image for months, taking sips of water, making faces, and spitting it out, then laughing our asses off. In sixth grade, Hughey organized games of "knockout" on the playground, where one person would bend over and hyperventilate, while the other would squeeze his chest from behind, making him, briefly, pass out. When Quentin Meeks hit his head on the asphalt on the way down and needed seven stitches, Sr. Beatrice, the principal, got wind of it, and made Hughey play by himself in the courtyard for the rest of the year, like a little convict.

For as long as I'd known him, Hughey had wanted to play professional football. In his basement, he'd work out until his arms and legs were shaking, then lie down on the floor until he had the strength to walk back up the stairs, where he'd gorge himself on hard-boiled eggs, cottage cheese, and canned tuna. That winter, I finally joined him, and the two of us spent hours down there, spotting and coaxing each other, paging through issues of *Muscle & Fitness* (smiling, striated photos of Frank Zane and Robby Robinson), while listening to Hughey's older sister's *Commodores* and *Earth, Wind, and Fire* albums.

He was the last of six kids, and nine years younger than his closest sibling. His father was a middle school principal, who'd played a few seasons in the CFL, and now walked with a limp. He always called me "young man," I think because he could never remember my name. His mother was a nurse at Beaumont, and very overweight. She wore enormous, brightly-colored caftans, and called me "honey." Their first three kids had turned out fine—two doctors and an engineer at GM— the next two, not so much. Hughey's older brother had joined the army to kick a heroin habit, and his sister had run away with the Moonies while still in high school. When the soldier came home in a body bag, and the Moonie came home and sat on the couch for a year eating Pringles and catching up on her soaps, Hughey's parents sort of threw in the towel, and from then on, he'd raised himself. He was the most self-sufficient kid you could imagine. He bought all his own clothes, cooked for himself, did his own laundry. At my house one day, he was appalled to see my mother ironing my shirts, and took it upon himself to teach me how to iron ("No, not up and down, *back and forth*"), further endearing himself to mom.

They loved him, my parents. He was confident and polite—"articulate," to use the white parents' favorite term—and he told great stories (a "raconteur," mom called him). Over dinner—which he ate more often at my house than his own, he and my dad, a European history professor at Wayne State, would argue politics and economics. A merciless capitalist, Hughey had no patience for most social programs and had scoffed when the nuns asked us to collect money in our mite boxes to give away to poor people. Since he was ten, he'd been getting up at five-thirty to deliver the *Free Press*, and had saved enough money to buy a motorcycle, which he intended to do on his sixteenth birthday. "Hughey's a heartless s.o.b.," my dad would joke, "but he is consistent." My mother, who spoke French and was a gourmet cook, got a kick out of him, too. I'd bring him home for lunch sometimes, and while mom served us up veal with sherry-mushroom sauce or ham and Gruyère soufflé (she went through a serious Julia Child phase), the three of us would watch *Gambit* on TV, with our host, Wink Martindale. Once, Wink announced that if the contestant got the answer correct, he'd win a new car. "And if your answer is incorrect," Hughey chimed in, "we will take away your presently-owned car." Mom about died laughing.

Some things, though, Hughey simply couldn't do on his own. When he made the finals in the state Punt, Pass, and Kick competition, it was my dad who drove him to the Silverdome to compete. When he needed a sponsor for Confirmation, it was my mom who stood behind him, her right hand on his shoulder. Hughey had realized that something was missing in his life, and just as he did with everything else he wanted, he went out and got it—a family, mine.

That summer, the summer we both turned thirteen, it was L.K. that Hughey wanted. I had my first job, working nights as a busboy at the Detroit Golf Club, and Hughey was unloading produce at Kroger's after his paper route, so we had our afternoons free, and after lifting weights one day, Hughey decided we should ride our bikes over to L.K.'s house.

She lived in a brick colonial over on Muirland, a somewhat stately house for our neighborhood. Ours was one of the last in the city still integrated. Since the riots ten years before, white families had been fleeing the city in droves, but in our neighborhood—anchored by St. Paul's—many had stayed. It wasn't all *kumbaya*, but in the summer, we had block parties, where the adults grilled on their front lawns, or sat around in aluminum chairs, smoking cigarettes and drinking Stroh's, while the kids rode their bikes in the street, ran through sprinklers, or if someone had arranged it through the city, splashed around in the Swimmobile. In the spring, we had alley clean-up days, and in the winter we shoveled the walks and driveways of our elderly neighbors. In the fall, on the night before Halloween each year—Devil's Night in Detroit, a traditional night of vandalism and fires—the men in the neighborhood stood guard on their front porches and in the alleys, some with guns, and others, like my father, with just flashlights or whistles.

It was Devil's Night the previous fall when I'd first seen L.K.'s father. He'd bought the house and moved in a few months before L.K. and her mother arrived. My own mother, who never drove, had picked me up from school that day. It was already getting dark when we drove by the Dougherty's old house, where the For Sale sign had been down for weeks. He was sitting out on the front stoop, a middle-aged, receding-hairline blond guy in a polyester suit and cheap, tasseled loafers. I saw mom's reaction go from "wow, white people moving *into* the neighborhood" to "uh, oh" as he picked a pistol off his lap, displayed it across his chest, and mad dogged us all the way down the block. It wasn't unusual to see our neighbors packing on Devil's Night, but it was the stare that unsettled us.

While Hughey rang the doorbell, I hung back and pretended to be very interested in their shrubbery. L.K.'s mother answered, the chain still on, and an I-don't-want-to-buy-any-raffle-tickets look. She was a tall, brown-haired woman in a blue housecoat, like a uniform, and she spoke in a thick Polish accent. When Hughey asked if L.K. was home, she looked flummoxed, and after a long pause, asked, "Why?" Hughey smiled and shrugged. "Just wanted to say hi." She left, and, after a much longer pause, L.K. came out, looking as nervous and confused as she did when Mrs. Crenshaw asked her to go outside and clap the erasers. "Avon calling," Hughey said. Then, "You order the chicken chow mein?" And finally, "Trick or treat!" which made L.K. smile, and before long, the three of us were sitting on her front stoop, talking.

At first, it was mostly Hughey doing the talking, but, as the summer wore on, L.K. opened up. For the first time, it seemed, this only child had someone to talk to. Slowly, the girl we'd been staring at for five months— this distant, mysterious beauty—became a real person. She told us about growing up in Krakow, how clean the city was, how little crime there was, but also how small their apartment had been, and how all it seemed they ate was *pierogi* and pickled vegetables. She told us how hard it was learning English, how she felt betrayed by words like "recipe" and "castle," that Mrs. Crenshaw had told her parents she should transfer to public school because she was "clearly special ed." L.K. showed us childhood photos, her fossil and igneous rock collections, an arrowhead she'd dug up in her back yard. She said she wanted to be an archaeologist, like her father had wanted to be, before the communists earmarked him for the food service industry. She said that there was no TV in her house, but always music, and we'd hear it sometimes, usually polka, sometimes classical. Her parents had wanted her to play the accordion, but she'd talked them into the piano, and had been taking lessons for years. We talked her into playing for us one day, and listened to her through an open living room window.

She played something she called, "Grande Valse brillante," and it was incredible to me that someone my age could do something like that. When I looked over at Hughey, he had his eyes closed, a smile on his face. We were never allowed inside their house—which always bothered Hughey, he thought it was because he was black—but her mother would bring us out lemonade and *punchkis*, which we loved. She started calling me "Roossell," and Hughey "Moossell"—her nickname, "muscle," for him. When L.K.'s father would get home—he owned a couple of KFC's on Livernois, and a bakery in Hamtramck—he'd make a big show out of stepping over our plates and glasses, grunt something to L.K. about dinner, and always make sure we saw the .38 he kept under his suit coat, for his frequent trips to the bank with the receipts.

Hughey was, as with everything else, way ahead of me with girls. He was making out in fourth grade, feeling girls up in sixth, oral sex by seventh, and on the cusp of losing his virginity that summer. There were girls—Phyllis Crump and Angie Brookins—who I knew he'd used for sex, and others—Margie Rimelspach and Jocelyn Bright—who I knew he'd liked, but with L.K., I'd never seen him so smitten. He talked about her all the time, and all he wanted to do was be with her. After our workouts, he'd shower and put on Hai Karate before we went over to see her. He talked Jimmy Ponkowki's mom into teaching him how to say, "You look beautiful" in Polish. For her birthday in July, Hughey dug deep into his motorcycle money, and bought L.K. a microscope—not the cheap plastic kind, either, but a heavy, steel one he'd had his doctor brother order from a lab—which her father promptly made her give him back.

When Hughey asked her why he had "such a stick up his ass," L.K. said her father wasn't such a bad guy, but that he'd had a hard life. When he was just a little boy, she said, he'd been taken from his parents by the Nazis, and sent to live with a German family, where he'd been beaten for speaking Polish. After the war, he'd made it back to Poland, but had never found his family. Because of this, L.K. said, he was very protective of his own family. In his business dealings too, she said, he'd become distrustful of certain people. "Like who?" I made the mistake of asking. She looked away. Jews, she said, he found "untrustworthy"; blacks, "unindustrious."

Hughey had been reclining on the steps, and sat up. "That's pretty ignorant," he said. "He has had some bad experiences," L.K. said, "with those people." She appeared to be defending him, and quickly caught herself. "But you are right, Hughey," she added, in her contractionless English, "it *is* extremely ignorant." The moment lingered uncomfortably. Hughey leaned back and closed his eyes. "Tell your dad," he said, "there's a KKK meeting tonight in Dearborn. They're electing a new Imperial Wizard, in case he's interested."

That night, I asked my father about what L.K. had said, about the Nazis. With dad, a comment about the weather could lead to an hour-long discourse on the Crimean War, so I wasn't too surprised to sit through half of World War II to learn that it was true: the Nazis had kidnapped children with certain desired features—blond hair and blue eyes, a specific shape to their skull—for "Germanization," while others could be sent to labor or concentration camps, where they could be murdered, or have medical experiments performed on them, just like the Jews. "You might say," dad said about L.K.'s father, "that he was one of the lucky ones." The Nazis, he explained, had a racial hierarchy that placed Aryans (the "Herrenvolk," or master race) at the top. He started to tell me more, but mom raised her hand and asked if there would be a midterm, and then it was time for bed.

Growing up in Detroit, it was impossible not to be aware of race. Walking home from school, I'd been honkey'd and cracker'd countless times by kids from the local public elementary school, and sometimes beaten up, while at the suburban barbershop where my mother took me for my haircuts, I'd listen to the barbers wax on about the "niggers," and how they should all be taken "back to Africa, whence they came." That summer, working at the Detroit Golf Club, I had to be blind not to see that all the members were white, and many of the employees black. Though there were jobs aplenty, and the money was good, Hughey had never worked there, and I never asked why.

One day, Hughey asked me to wait at the sidewalk, while he rang L.K.'s doorbell. He wanted to ask her to go with him. She refused, though, playing up the friendship/big brother angle on him, and it cut Hughey deep. He began lashing out at both of us. He started making up obscene counter-lyrics to the polka music coming from her house ("round, firm, and fully packed / it was hanging from my sack / someone stole my kishka!"), and whenever L.K. said something remotely unintelligent, he'd call her, "special ed." With me, whenever I hesitated to do something he wanted—distract the cashier at Pelzer's while he pinched a forty, or keep watch outside Phyllis Crump's house while she gave him head—Hughey would skip the wheedling and cajoling, and go straight to humiliation. "What's that between your legs, Russell?" he'd ask. "Is it a dick? Or is it a pussy?"

Secretly, I was glad she'd turned him down. A lot was changing for me, too. My older brother, Danny, had been the kind of kid who performed magic tricks, acted in school plays, and with very little coaxing, would sing "Hey, Jude" at talent shows and my parents' parties. He was universally-liked, and a doting older brother who, for the first seven years of my life, did all the talking for me. Shortly after he died, Hughey came into my life, and it was out of one shadow, into another. Maybe it was puberty, maybe my first job, or maybe L.K., but that summer, something clicked. I looked in the mirror and saw not just hair on my pits and around my balls, but with all the weightlifting, I had cuts and veins on my forearms and biceps. My face didn't look so soft anymore, my cheeks so pinchable.

Then, too, there were the erections. At St. Paul's, we'd been taught that our carnal urges needed to be "sublimated"—redirected into something positive, like chores or Our Fathers—and that in no case were we boys supposed to touch our erections, and for years, I'd reached for a piece of toilet paper in the middle of the night, in order to sinlessly aim my piss boner at the toilet. Now, though, the erections were different, diurnal and unpredictable, and could not be sublimated simply by emptying my bladder. Watching episodes of *Wonder Woman* in the den with my parents, paging through the illustrations in Danny's old *Mad Magazines*, or simply catching a glimpse of the right billboard or album cover, and there I was. Alone in the house one rainy day, I wandered into my father's office, lay on his sheepskin rug, and with photos of FDR and Winston Churchill looking down on me, humped it until I came. It felt like knockout, only better.

In August, when we had a few days in the nineties, L.K. came out one afternoon in shorts and bare feet, her hair long, shiny, and ribbonless, a slight hoarseness to her voice from a lingering summer cold. "Boys," she said, "I thought you would never get here." I think it surprised even her, her use of an American idiom, the forwardness of her comment, but she didn't shy away from it, and leaned back, stretched out her legs, and lifted her face to the sun, like a girl in a Coppertone ad. It was at that moment I realized that I, too, was in love with her.

By football season, Hughey had gotten so big that he was no longer allowed to play in our CYO games, where the league had a weight limit. He played in just one game, a non-league, pre-season one, and hit the opposing team's running back so hard, he knocked him out. Their coach called his team off the field, they got on their bus, and left. While Hughey was relegated to charting plays and substitutions on the sidelines, I snuck into a starting cornerback position.

In the fall issue of our blurry, mimeographed school newspaper— the "Super Snooper" section—it was proclaimed that "Hughey Harris, Steve Marable, and Russell Brennan have captured the hearts of the girls in junior high." I had my first kiss, Dana Pruitt, a black girl, behind the St. Vincent De Paul bin one morning before school. She put her tongue in my ear, just as the bell rang. Margie Rimelspach grapevined that she wanted to go with me, but I grapevined back that I wasn't interested. I was starting to think I had a chance with L.K.

Our friendship with her had done wonders for her social status, too, and on the playground that first month, we'd see her with Margie, Jocelyn, and the other popular eighth grade girls in their spot along the Livernois fence. A game had begun that involved tying little pieces of yarn around each other's wrists—yellow yarn meant that someone was your friend, red yarn that you liked them. L.K. had offered Hughey her yellow yarn, but he'd refused, saying he was "holding out for red."

Our own friendship, mine and Hughey's, was deteriorating. I'd grown tired of his insults, tired of my role as his fool, his wing man, his lookout. In the face of his manipulations, I now stood firm, or simply walked away. Worse, for him, I stopped inviting him over, and, when my parents asked about him, I said they should invite him over themselves, have him move in, adopt him for all I cared.

By mid-October, our football season was winding down. We were 2-6, Hughey had dislocated his shoulder, and I'd lost my starting position to a sixth grader. "Hey, Russ," Hughey said, "why don't we skip practice and hang out?" It was a warm, hazy day, Indian summer, and we were out on the playground, staring across at the Livernois fence, which wasn't the same without L.K. there—her cold had turned into pneumonia, and she'd been home all week recovering. That morning, we'd taken our high school entrance exams, and Hughey and I had listed different schools as our first choice. It saddened me, this reminder of us going our separate ways. I saw Hughey bracing for my usual excuse. "Yeah, okay," I said.

After school, we ducked over to a scrubby little playground off Six Mile, the kind with broken glass and cigarillo filters all over the ground, the word "fuck" scratched into every conceivable surface. At one time, they'd tried for a "space" theme to the place, and in the middle was a tall slide with a rocket ship-like canopy. Hughey suggested we go up there to check out the view, and when we did, he produced a joint that he'd stolen from his sister's purse. It was classic Hughey, withholding information that he knew would make me chicken out. He sat down and lit up. "It's easy, Russ, watch." He took a hit, leaned his head back, exhaled, and held it out to me. I'd snuck a few of my mom's Winstons over the years, but never this. Still, I couldn't bear to go back to our old dynamics, so, without thinking, I took it, and inhaled. We passed it back and forth, and when we were done, Hughey smiled and said, "Congratulations, grasshopper!"

Soon, our little rocket ship lifted off, and we were soaring above our neighborhood. "There's my house!" I said. "There's the team, practicing," Hughey said. "Hey, Mr. Kirkland," I yelled. "Fuck you!" "Look," Hughey said, his voice softening, "there's L.K.'s house." He turned to me: his eyes were red, sleepy. "Let's go see her," he said. "She's sick," I laughed. "Plus, we reek." Hughey thought for a second. "I can fix this," he said. He reached into his pocket and took out his little spray bottle of Hai Karate. He closed his eyes, sprayed himself all over, then pointed the nozzle at me. "Don't you fucking—" I said, but of course, he did, and there was nowhere for me to hide. "Dick," I said. "I'm going home." I sounded pouty, unmanly. "*Punchkis*, Russ," Hughey said, "Think about the *punchkis*." We hadn't eaten since before noon. "Besides," Hughey said, "you can't go home. You're supposed to be at practice."

As we walked, we picked up acorns, and threw them at stop signs and parked cars. There was a warm glow over our neighborhood, sunlight filtering through the trees, the smell of burning leaves. I felt happy and relaxed, and vowed to smoke pot every day for the rest of my life.

"You know what I wish?" Hughey said.

"What?"

"I wish that everyone on earth was the same race, the same color. That there was just one race, one color."

I'd never heard him get sentimental like this, and I felt tender toward Hughey for the first time. In his mind, I knew, race was what stood between him and L.K. But I'd already decided that, when she came back to school, I was going to ask L.K. to go with me. If being white gave me an advantage with her, so be it.

"That'd be sweet," I said.

He threw his acorn at a car, where it pinged off the hood. "Shit hurts," he said, wincing and rubbing his shoulder.

At L.K.'s house, we rang the doorbell and knocked, but no one answered. "Maybe they're at the doctor's," I said. We sat down on the stoop to commiserate. It was getting dark. My stomach growled. "I think it's cassoulet tonight," I finally said, standing up. "Want to come over?"

But Hughey wasn't listening. He got up, and walked around the side of the house. Most of the homes in our neighborhood had been built in the thirties, and had milk chutes—small, square openings with latched metal doors on either side—built into them. I'd shown Hughey once how, if locked out of my own house, I could open the exterior door, pound on the interior one hard enough to jar loose the latch, open it, and climb through. The Kuplicki's chute was next to their side door. Hughey opened the chute, tried my trick, and after a couple of hard hits, it sprang open. He looked inside, then back at me. "You'll have to do it," he said. "There's no way I'll fit."

"Are you crazy?" I said. Then, stupidly, "We don't even know where they keep the *punchkis*."

"In the bathroom, Russ. Just climb in, and open the door for me."

I looked inside: there was a landing, then just a few steps up to the kitchen. "No way," I said.

"It's cool, Russ," Hughey said. He stared at the house for a few moments, then started walking away. That's when I realized it wasn't about the *punchkis* for him. He just wanted to go inside their house, to do what had been forbidden to him, for reasons he found intolerable.

"Hey," I called, and before he could turn around, dove in.

I landed on my hands, got up, and opened the door. I scrambled up the steps, and, like a thief on TV, quickly began opening and closing cabinets—Campbell's soup, Dinty Moore, Rice-a-Roni, sugar, and spices, but no *punchkis*. I turned for the fridge: Hughey was casually looking over their photos. One in particular had caught his eye, one L.K. had shown us earlier, that we'd both lingered over. It was L.K., sitting in a field somewhere, Poland, I guess, looking up at the camera, and smiling. The photo was black and white and unremarkable, except for the fact that she looked *completely adorable*. I reached for it just before he did, grabbed it, and shoved it into my pocket. Hughey turned, and for a second, I thought he was going to hit me, but then we heard the front door opening. We ran to the side door, bolted out, and kept running, all the way home.

That night, I couldn't sleep. I'd skipped practice, smoked weed, broken into someone's house, and stolen something. Instead of feeling guilty, I felt exhilarated. I slid out of bed, and did pushups until I was exhausted, then went into the bathroom and admired my flushed muscles. Back in my room, I stared at my new photo for a while before turning off the lights. Just before falling asleep, my eyes adjusting to the darkness, I looked around— at the Snoopy and Woodstock "Best Friends" poster, the pictures-of-me mobile I'd built in a long ago art class, the fluorescent Tot Finder sticker affixed to my window—and thought, *Really, Russell? Really?*

The next day, walking home after practice, a brown Cutlass pulled up next to us, and L.K.'s father got out. He walked over and pointed his pistol in Hughey's face. Hughey didn't even blink. "I smell you in my house," he said. "You come near my house or daughter again"—he paused, made a firing motion—"pow." To cover his bases, he glared at me for a second, then got back in his car and left. We continued walking, and gradually my legs stopped shaking. "I'm hungry," Hughey said. "What's your mom making, tonight?"

A few days later, when L.K. came back to school, she cornered me and asked if I had anything to do with the break-in. No, I lied. Then I asked her to go with me. She said yes, and I did what I'd been wanting to do all summer, maybe since I first saw her: I buried my face in her long, blond hair, rubbed my cheek against it, ran my fingers through it, inhaled it.

Her parents had her on lockdown, and I had it in mind to spare Hughey's feelings, so we tried to keep things secret—passing notes, stealing kisses before school, holding hands under the lunch table. But it wasn't enough, so I hatched a plan where I told my parents I'd made the basketball team, and L.K. told hers she'd joined the band, and, as long as she was out front of school at 5:00 each night for her father to pick her up, and I walked in the door around the same time, we had an hour and half together. The problem was finding someplace to go. We tried the rocket ship slide, but the druggies and winos that came by scared L.K., so we tried the playground at Hampton, the local elementary school, but got honkey'd and otherwise harassed, and I almost got into a fight, so, as it was getting colder, we tried a Hardees on Six Mile, but the manager said we'd have to order more than a small fries if we planned on staying for an hour.

"You don't have to keep hiding it from me," Hughey, who really was playing on the basketball team, said to me one day. "I know you're going with L.K., I'm not stupid." It was a Saturday, and we were lifting weights in his basement. By this time, Hughey had maxed out the space on his barbell, and had begun tying weights to the ends of it with twine looped through the holes. I couldn't even spot him, it was so much weight. He seemed okay with things, so I told him about my dilemma with L.K. He squeezed out the last few reps on a set of bench presses, sat up, and ran a sweat band across his forehead. "You can bring her here," he said. "My parents and sister won't be home, and I'll be at practice." I looked around: there was a bean bag chair, a couch, a lava lamp, a clock radio, and the record player. Hughey's parents kept the thermostat set to tropical, so it was even cozy warm. "The spare key's under the Geranium, in the garage."

L.K. and I, we clung to each other down there like two drowning swimmers, a pair of repressed loners who'd spent too much time in the shadows of others, or alone in our rooms with our rocks or pet lizards. With Lionel Ritchie—less sappy, more soulful then—crooning to us in the dark, we opened our mouths to each other, roamed our hands over each other's bodies, and ground our crotches together. After, I'd lie there and watch the numbers flip on the clock radio, dreading when it hit 4:40, and we'd have to get up and head our separate ways, L.K. back to school, and me, home.

We went on like this for almost two months, until the last day of school before Christmas break, a blindingly sunny day following two days of off-and-on snowfall. She and I were walking to Hughey's house for the last of our—to use a word of my mother's—*rendez-vous*, before a two-week hiatus I was dreading. Everyone else seemed to be in a good mood, though, including Hughey, who bounded up to us, put his arms around us, and announced that not only had practice been cancelled, but he'd procured another joint from his sister's purse, and not only could we smoke it with him, but we could do it at his house, since his parents had left that morning for their timeshare in Florida. Things had been kind of weird the past few weeks with L.K., her begging off a couple of our visits, saying she wanted to hang out with her new friends ("It is not good every day, Roossell, to have you on top of me"), while I couldn't comprehend anything better than dry humping with her in Hughey's basement. I'd been up most of the night, worrying what was going on. I looked over at her. L.K. shrugged.

It was her first time, too, so I played the expert, and before long the three of us were laughing our asses off, making fun of teachers, nuns, and each other. We made L.K. say things like "Blow me" and "Yo mama," because they sounded hilarious in her accented English, and because she had the giggles so bad she could barely talk. Hughey fired up the turntable, and we took turns dancing to "September" and "Shining Star," while the other two clapped, just like on *Soul Train*. L.K. was terrible, but she didn't seem to care. Nobody did, and I felt that closeness again, like I'd felt that day with Hughey, but now for both of them. At a certain point, I sat on the bean bag chair, leaned my head back, and drifted off. When I woke up, it was dark, "Reasons" was playing, and I looked at the clock radio: 5:34. I sat up. By the light of the lava lamp, I could see L.K. and Hughey slow dancing. Hughey leaned down and kissed her, and she kissed him back. I don't know if they even noticed me leaving, and I didn't care.

Outside, it was cold, but my face was hot with humiliation. *Do not cry*, I thought. I may have screamed or moaned, probably something in between. It was snowing again, I saw Christmas lights in people's windows, and I thought about how lonely and miserable this vacation was going to be. I'd gone just over a block, when I saw the brown Cutlass coming slowly up the street. *Fuck him*, I thought. I was ready for anything. He stopped in front of me, and rolled down his window. He looked angry and scared. He asked me if I'd seen his daughter. Yes, I said, I had. And I told him exactly where.   ❧

THE VEGETARIAN

Matthew Salesses

Full of rage, I used to write op-eds. I wrote them not because I was angry, but because, honestly, I wanted to share anger with others. I wanted to change people's minds, stir up their lives, overthrow the kind of limp thinking that keeps us captive to society's poor imagination. I had some success getting these essays published, and when people shared them in their social media feeds I felt like I was doing some good in the world. Then I started to realize that the people who shared these essays and who read them already shared my anger; their minds were not changed, their lives were not stirred, they believed they were right, and my essays allowed them to feel even more right, to become even more calcified. They didn't need to change any further, because they were already enlightened. I didn't share this belief.

What I wondered was simple: how does one write something that compels a person to tear down her life, continually, that not only fosters sympathy for a character who tears down her own life, but also teaches the socially conscious reader to do so, too? Not write *about* resistance, but write in a way that encourages a reader to resist the manicured surfaces of their lives?

There is a book I read last year: *The Vegetarian*, by Han Kang, which won the 2016 Man Booker International Prize. It is about a woman who decides to become a vegetarian. No one around her wants her to do this. In the first third of the book, her husband, in first person, despises and does terrible things to her, because she will not give up giving up meat. In most books, the story is about the narrator. As I read *The Vegetarian*, I found myself sympathizing through only the entrapment of first person. We see as he sees. What I had to do, if I did not want to hate myself as I hated this narrator, was to resist the *I*.

The second third of the book moves to third-person, following the perspective of the woman's brother-in-law, who is far less hateful. At first, it seems a relief. But soon the brother-in-law becomes obsessed with the woman. He's married, with kids, but he wants to sleep with his sister-in-law. He is an artist and he wants to turn her into a work of art, and as he starts to manipulate her, the same resistance is needed—if you let your guard down, you will find yourself allied with another man, less obviously hateful but no less terrible.

The last third of the novel returns to first-person, through the woman's sister, who loves her and is trying to take care of her. By this time the vegetarian does not want to eat at all—one might think she has gone through trauma enough for her desires. Our new narrator has to commit her own sister, where the staff violently force her to eat in horrible detail. The narrator would rather not hurt her beloved sister, but this is the price of staying alive as a human being. Finally we have someone who means well, but by now we want only for everyone to leave the woman alone to do what she wants. ❧

Dummies

Greg Ames

The word ventriloquism comes from the Latin terms *venter* and *loqui*, literally meaning "belly speak." Dummies, therefore, are often referred to as "tummy talkers," because they "speak from the stomach" and give voice to previously unexpressed thoughts and feelings. The doll speaks in a more frank and open manner than her human counterpart can, given the handler's need to save face and follow established social conventions of propriety. The dummy, therefore, is the truthteller, the oracle, in this contentious relationship, and the "master" is soon revealed to be the subservient one. The audience sits in silent anticipation, eager to see the handler outwitted by a dummy who gives voice to the hidden and hitherto unacknowledged needs of heart, stomach, and genitals.

— Elaine Blabler, *Hearing the Unspoken Voice: The Ancient Art of Ventriloquism*

When she was eleven years old, my older sister Cassie carried a ventriloquist's dummy with her wherever she went. The dummy's name was Marilyn, and at first nobody had the heart to tell Cassie that Marilyn was not really a dummy, but a charred log from our fireplace. Every night Cassie slept in her narrow bed with this splintered wedge of burnt wood. She cuddled with it on the sofa while watching soap operas and sitcoms, and she left ashy smudges on everything she touched, from the refrigerator door to her once-white gerbils. Cassie's homeroom teacher was concerned. The school psychologist, Nancy Palermo, asked my father if we had recently lost any family members to a house blaze or fiery car crash, anything like that. My father said, "Not exactly." Ms. Palermo wanted to see Cassie three times a week after school for private consultations.

We lived in a squat, crumbling yellow brick house surrounded by tiger lilies. All the houses on Hood Lane were the same size. Our street appealed to young couples just starting out, elderly folks in pajamas, recovering addicts taking life one day at a time, and struggling small business owners. There were no block parties or street fairs, but every now and then some drunk kid would crash his father's car into a tree, and we'd all gather around swimming in the headlights.

My mother's absence from our lives—she said she was just getting her head straight in Tampa, Florida—forced my father to become the sole nurturer in our household, a terrible burden added to his already overwhelming duties as paragon and provider. He hadn't touched a vodka tonic in over fourteen months. But when my mother took off for Florida, a move that took us all by surprise, Dad stopped going to his Don't Drink meetings and stayed home with us.

"You listen to me," he said from the helm of his armchair, unable to ignore my sister's strange new hobby any longer. "That's not a proper dummy." He rose to his feet and stood above us. "Just look at it, for God's sake. It doesn't even have a mouth or even a face."

When my sister didn't respond, Dad changed tactics. In a softer voice, he said, "The other kids will make fun of you. You don't want that— do you, honey?"

He unwrapped a lollipop and paced in front of Cassie, who was seated on the family room sofa clutching Marilyn to her breast like some horribly burned infant. I sat crosslegged on the floor at Dad's feet, paying close attention because I knew that someday I'd need to write all this down, just in case somebody asked me why I behave the way I do. "Ventriloquists are . . ." He thought for a moment. "Annoying," he said. "And nobody really likes them."

Cassie brooded, arms folded, on the sofa. "That's not true," she said. "A lot of people like them."

"Sure, the dimwits in the audience eat it up with a spoon," he said, "but only because they're embarrassed for the ridiculous sap who totes a stupid dummy around. Really. It's old hat. Fifties Vegas crap. That type of humor doesn't appeal to us anymore. We're much more sophisticated in our interests nowadays, Cassandra." He hooked his thumbs into the belt loops of his jeans. "And I'm only talking about the traditional stuff. What you're attempting here . . . Well, believe me, honey. Nobody will have any patience for some confused little kid with a burnt log for a freakin' dummy. That's for damn sure."

"I like them!" Cassie said, her braces glittering. "I know you don't care what I like, Dad, but ventriloquists make me happy." She squeezed Marilyn tighter. "I'm gonna be a world famous ventriloquist someday, whether you like it or not."

"Honey," he said, "it's burnt wood." He chopped the blade of his hand through the air. "Am I the only one in this house who sees that? Just look at that thing. It doesn't even have a mouth or—or even a face!" He turned to me. "Wayne, could you back me up here?"

"Dummies," I said, smiling. "Dummies, dummies, dummies."

My father stared at me for a few seconds without speaking.

"Mom would let me do it," Cassie said. "Mom would encourage me."

My father twirled the lollipop stick in his mouth. "I just don't get the attraction of ventriloquism. Really. I'm at a loss here. I mean, it wasn't even cool in my day. And now? Let's face it, it's not even in the conversation."

He looked to me again. Whatever expression he saw on my nine-year-old face didn't invite an easy alliance.

"You two need to learn about 'cool.' You know what the coolest kids in any school do?" Dad shoved both hands in the back pockets of his jeans. "They sing and dance. Look back in time, look forward: doesn't matter. What will the cool kids be doing a hundred years from now?"

"Singing and maybe dancing?" I said, trying to catch Cassie's eye, hoping she'd laugh with me.

"That's right, son. That's right," he said, smiling back at me. "They will be singing and dancing in the streets. You can't hold them back. Don't even try."

"I won't," I said.

"Smart. Because it wouldn't do you any good."

My sister hugged Marilyn to her breast. "You guys are both such jerks," she said in a small voice.

"What did I do?" I said.

"Okay, okay, fine, if you insist on pursuing this," he said, making a grand concession, the lollipop bobbing up and down in his mouth, "just ditch the log, and I'll buy you a real dummy at the clown shop or whatever, and you can—"

"Stop it!" Cassie pushed past him. Swinging her pointed elbows, she ran out of the family room and stomped up the stairs, trailing a whiff of scorch behind her. We heard her bedroom door slam shut.

"Well, she's got a flair for the dramatic, I'll give her that," he said. "But I'm worried about that girl. What is she trying to prove here?"

Stroking his goatee, that gingery eruption of hair on his face, Dad looked out the family room window at the snowplowed street. Cassie's strange behavior had called into question so much that he had taken for granted, including his own coolness. He was forty-four years old, a marketing director for Studio Arena Theatre, a job that allowed him to dress and act like an artist—ponytail, earrings, jeans—yet still collect a businessman's steady paycheck. He liked avant-garde theater, but he was not hip enough to deal with the grotesque in his own home. He bit into the lollipop. Flakes of green candy clung to the inverted triangle of hair beneath his lower lip. He would have welcomed my mother's input in a situation like this. Her absence galled him. He looked down at me and frowned. "And what do you find so amusing, mister?"

I had become a watchdog for adult hypocrisy. I spent up to twelve hours a day studying the erratic behavior of grownups with a smirk on my face.

My father hitched up his sagging jeans and squatted before me like an aging baseball catcher. He put his hands on my shoulders. "Let's have us a little chat," he said, "man to man. Now, I know you two are a team, but we're all on the same team, right?" I smelled the sour apple of his lollipop. "Is your sister still popular at that school? What do the other kids say about her?"

"She has lots of friends," I said, and then corrected myself. "She used to."

He nodded. "Minor setback. She'll win them back. So, who are the most popular kids nowadays? The singers, the dancers? Or the jocks?"

I shrugged.

"The nerds?" He smiled. "Have the nerds finally risen to the top?"

"Every cool kid is different, Dad."

"Right, right. It's the age of specialization. She's taking a big risk with this log thing, but who knows? It might pay off. You think it could?"

I was the wrong person to ask. My inability to keep up with the latest trends always unnerved my father. The public schools, in his opinion, were a hotbed of ingenuity, a testing ground where a tribe of potential superstars sparred over the future of our culture's rites and rituals. But I was too busy to worry about any of that. My mother had moved to Florida, without warning, and I'd become the unofficial archivist of her debris. I inventoried the baubles on her bedside table. I straightened the photo I'd pinned on the fridge beneath a pineapple magnet. Nights, in my bedroom, I read her left-behind books, especially the photocopied working scripts from the roles she'd played at the theater. I fixated on her tiny pencil-scrawled notes in the margins: "Build." "Energy, energy, energy." "Brokenhearted."

"So what's your gambit to achieve popularity in school?" my father asked.

"My what?"

"Your sister has Marilyn. What sets you apart from the pack?"

"Nothing," I said.

"That's loser talk. Think about where there's a demand, a need, and then give the people what they want. Are there any singers and dancers in your grade?"

"I don't know." A tired sigh escaped me. "I guess."

Roosevelt Middle School, a four-story moron factory on the west side of town, warehoused close to four thousand kids, and featured a substantial population of head bangers, gasoline sniffers, bullies and other future felons. Mr. Brummer, the head security guard, roamed the corridors eyeballing every backpack and lunchbox with the institutional distrust of an El Paso border guard. A cleft-chinned chain smoker with a diamond stud in his left earlobe, Brummer the Bummer would sometimes stop me in the hall, invade my personal space and ask an inane question just so he could see if my pupils were dilated. I didn't know if he recognized the future stoner in me and was trying to prevent this terrible fate, or if all his chatter about illicit substances and "what they could do to a boy" actually drove me to the bong in high school.

"You kids have so much to offer," Dad said, "but in my opinion you're selling yourselves short."

He tucked the sticky lollipop stick behind his ear, one of the oddest moves I'd ever seen him make. Though twenty years have passed since that day, I still sometimes think about that hapless white stick balanced over my father's ear like an unsmoked cigarette, giving him the look of a street tough in an old Hollywood movie, a ne'er-do-well loitering outside the pool hall.

Dad patted my shoulder, stood up, and walked out of the room. In the kitchen, a cupboard door banged shut. "God, grant me the serenity..." he said. A moment later he returned, his cheek bulging with a fresh lollipop.

"I'm gonna check on Cassie," I said, rising from the floor.

"Okay! Now you're talking." He nodded in approval. "Good man," he called after me. "That's the spirit! Report back to me afterwards and we'll compare notes."

I climbed the stairs and knocked on my sister's closed bedroom door. "Get lost, Wayne," she said, sniffling. "I just wanna be alone."

I opened the door and stepped in. The bonfire aroma blended with all the other exotic smells of her bedroom: damp towels and washcloths; nail polish remover; sticky bottles of cheap perfume spot welded to the dresser; cherry and grape lip gloss. She'd moved these items from Mom's dressing table to her own, along with some costume jewelry and a handheld mirror. Chest down on her bed, her ankles crossed in the air behind her, Cassie flicked through the pages of a *Seventeen* magazine. Marilyn was on the once-white pillowcase, just under Cassie's swaying feet. In the virginal setting of her bedroom, this black log was as conspicuous and disconcerting as a man standing naked in traffic.

I sat down on the smudged pink comforter and placed my hand on her back, the way Dad sometimes did with me when I had a nightmare.

"I have gum in my room," I said, trying not to brag. "Hubba Bubba and Bubble Yum. I'll give you a piece. What's your favorite flavor?"

She ignored me.

"I might have Juicy Fruit, but I'd have to check first."

"I don't want any *gum*. God."

We sat in silence for half a minute, my sister smothering her tears while I searched for the right words.

"Want me to try to paint your toenails again?" I asked at last. "I can do it better this time."

"Just leave me alone, Wayne. God, can't I have any privacy in this house?"

"I wish! Tell me about it," I said, employing two of her favorite expressions back-to-back to ingratiate myself with her. And for about three seconds, I gawked at the oily burnt stains on her pillowcases, knowing, even then, that they would never be clean again. "Hey, Cassie," I said. "You're right. Ventriloquists *are* cool."

She swung her face toward me. "Really? You think so?"

"Definitely." I nodded. "Yep."

"I've been practicing every night. I'm getting better, too. I think I'm actually pretty good."

"Well, that's what it takes. To get good, I mean."

"Do you want to see me do a routine?"

I told her I did, and honestly, I did. Even though my sister's armpit sweat smelled foreign to me now and zits had colonized her chin, I still considered her my best friend. We hadn't spent much time together since Mom had left for Florida. Cassie's bedroom had become off limits. No boys allowed. So I felt honored by her invitation to watch a private performance.

She propped the burnt log on her lap. Her oily forehead featured a few ashy fingerprint swirls. Her smudged yellow T-shirt called to mind a demented crossbreed of Charlie Brown and Pigpen. "Okay," she said. "Here goes." She took a deep breath and shouted, "It's a nice day today, isn't it, Marilyn?" She bounced her left knee once, hard, and ashes fell to the rug.

"Mmm-hmm!" Marilyn said.

Cassie looked down at Marilyn as though she were a newborn baby. "Do you like going to school, Marilyn?"

"Mmm-hmm!" Marilyn said.

"That's good." Cassie laughed. "School is important. But it's also really tough for a lot of people. Will you be ready for seventh grade, you think?"

Marilyn thought about it for a moment, considered the possibilities before answering definitively: "Mmm-hmm!"

My sister stared at me with raised eyebrows. "So? What do you think?" A loose strand of blond hair fell over her eyes. She pushed her lower lip out and blew the curl back.

"Wow," I said.

"Right? I'm getting good at it. Mrs. Palermo says I have a 'unique talent.'

"Remember when I told you about Mister Charleston and Woody coming for assembly? They were really great and everybody loved it when Mr. Charleston drank that orange juice and Woody sang 'Feelings.' Whoa oh oh feelings." She searched my eyes for an answer and motioned to her oppressor downstairs. "And if I love it," she said, "shouldn't that be what matters? I want to get really good before Mom comes back, so she can see what I can do."

On an intuitive level I understood my sister's sorrow. On the other hand, I found ventriloquism weird and scary. And though I agreed, in principle, with my father's assessment of the craft, I tried to remain neutral to protect everyone's feelings. Even at nine, I recognized the necessity of self-preservation.

"Why won't he ever support me?" she asked. "Why does he do that?"

I shrugged. "Because all grownups are dicks and I hate them?"

Cassie smiled at me. I smiled back. Then we both broke out snorting and cracking up. At that moment, we were as close as we had been since Mom left for Florida.

It didn't last.

"Well, if Mom's not back soon," Cassie said, "I'm going to Florida to live with her. She'll let me do what I want."

My sister had once been popular and funny, a straight-A student who had always been a favorite of her teachers. Her high standing had given me, her little brother, an extra boost. Left to my own devices, I was a brooding, bookish daydreamer trying to read *Waiting For Godot* and *The Bald Soprano* in my room while other boys shot pellet guns by the railroad tracks. Sometimes I tried to read my mom's existential philosophy books, too, and as a consequence of this unsupervised research, I began to suspect that God, like Santa Claus and the Easter Bunny, was just another big fat lie, a threat perpetuated by adults who wanted to keep children docile. I waited for the day when Dad would sit me down and explain that heaven and the devil and happiness and sex also didn't exist. It occurred to me that grownups had no idea what they were doing, especially when it came to raising children, and I studied their alien behavior with cold objectivity, hoping that by understanding the nature of hypocrisy, I might not go through life terrified of absolutely everything.

As far as I could tell my sister was a lost cause. A training bra dangled over the back of her desk chair. She couldn't pass a mirror without poking her hair, checking her teeth, inspecting her profile. Her once-smooth face was now shiny with grime and pustules. Something secret and horrible was going on in her bedroom at night, something that didn't include me.

I wanted Cassandra to go back to normal, to give up ventriloquism and become my best friend again, but she was as stubborn as everybody else in the family. Nobody could tell her what to do. She needed to believe she'd made the choice on her own. My job, as I saw it, was simply to plant the seed and skedaddle.

"You know," I said, rising to my feet, "it's okay that you're embarrassing our family with all this crazy stuff. Because Mom isn't ever coming back. She couldn't wait to ditch us." I motioned with my chin to the burnt log in my sister's arms. "Probably for reasons like this. We're freaks."

I left her bedroom with hardly a backward glance. I trotted down the carpeted stairs, kicked open the back door, and hopped down the slushy cement steps. Snow crunched underneath my sneakers in the driveway.

My father followed me outside. "What did you find out, champ?" he called out. "Let's compare notes."

I sprinted down the driveway and dove behind a snow bank, knowing that I had broken away from her, too, my last link to the idea of a family.

"Wayne!" My father stood on the steps and hugged himself for warmth. "Come here, son. I want to ask you some questions."

Ignoring his call, I lay flat on the sidewalk behind the snowbank, holding my breath, swallowing my words, until my father cursed at the sky and returned inside.

From that night until just now, I have been on my own. ❧

Sacramento

Elizabeth Gold

It was the year men landed on the moon and nobody
could understand why the Revolution hadn't arrived yet
then he took the bus to Sacramento.
Oh, Sacramento, time machine, dialed back
to his childhood, where red-faced, stiff
haired men and women drove sun-struck streets
in big American cars and a girl—homecoming queen?—
waved her white gloved hand at the crowds as if simply being
herself was gift enough for anybody.
Across the ocean, war. A country burning so we'd stay free.
The traffic light changed. The ice cream shop had introduced
three more flavors. That was your news,
in Sacramento. He took the bus back to San Francisco.
Daredevil hills. Hummingbirds. Radiant blur that beat
by your ear urgent messages: *Here. Yes. Must. Now.*
Even birds knew what was right, in San Francisco.
But that night, in his knock-kneed wooden house
that smelled of dope and patchouli and lentil loaf (sodden,
like something undug) and the others were talking
Che and any minute it was all going to go, *man*, explode,
and about time, too, mean old America, he found himself
pondering Sacramento: those wide wide streets and the flags,
and the big oaks the pioneers planted casting their green
shade, and the homecoming queen waving
her soft hand and smiling that sugar
sweet smile for him. Only for him.

Big Meteor Storm Heading Our Way

Elizabeth Gold

These are not crumbs strewn across the universe.
There is no cottage to track our way back to,
no dice, no alphabet. The static on the radio
has no secret messages. I have never seen the face
of Jesus in a loaf of bread or traffic light
in my life. And that night, violet,
overripe with the end of August
when I saw between two skyscrapers
a lit blimp like a fruit so heavy
it was ready to drop into my hands,
the Good Year emblazoned on its side,
wasn't sent to me. Didn't mean anything.
This morning I read the headline and tonight
I'm climbing to the roof, past locked
doors, the fraying welcome mats.
And if I should say *beautiful* when the sky
shoots with white shrapnel, it means
nothing, except there are lights
ricocheting above the kitchen windows,
and it is, it is.

NIGHTMARE ABBEY By Thomas Love Peacock

Dylan Hicks

It would be stunting and perverse to prefer minor books to major ones as a hard-and-fast rule, but there are understandable reasons for doing so much, let's say a majority, of the time. You might be suspicious of ambition, averse to pomposity, greedy for signs that your own talents, so obviously short of genius, might nonetheless produce quietly distinguished—even enduring—works of the second tier. Cynthia Ozick, quoted by Phillip Lopate in *The Art of the Personal Essay,* wrote that "a delectable preciousness (not inevitably a pejorative, if you consider Max Beerbohm), or a calculated smallness, or an unstoppable scheme of idiosyncrasy, comic or other—or simply the persnickety insistence on *being* minor—can claim permanence as easily as the more capacious qualities of a Proust or a Joyce." That seems right, if too defensive; part of the allure of minor books is that their claims, to permanence and everything, are by definition humbler than those of the great. Another part of that allure is that minor books mitigate the problem of readerly obligation and disappointment: if you're hunting for works of compellingly uneven modesty rather than canonical life changers, you're less likely to walk away unsatisfied, and if you do, you can safely blame the book's defects rather than your own.

Thomas Love Peacock's satirical roman á clef *Nightmare Abbey* is a great—which is to say, a very good—minor novel. Published in 1818, it takes gentle aim at fashionably dour romanticism, assembling fictional surrogates of some of the movement's leading figures at the melancholy Christopher Glowry's country house, "a venerable family-mansion, in a highly picturesque state of semi-dilapidation." The book's brooding protagonist, Mr. Glowry's heir Scythrop, is patterned after Shelley, a good friend of Peacock who received the book with thick-skinned enthusiasm. Now in the early stages of a writing career, Scythrop has recently published a treatise "in which his meanings were carefully wrapt up in the monk's hood of transcendental technology, but filled with hints of matter deep and dangerous, which he thought would set the nation in a ferment." He's not discouraged that the book has instead sold a modest seven copies, seeing in the number a mystically favorable auspice.

Nightmare Abbey's plot, of secondary interest to Peacock, sets up a love triangle of Scythrop and two women: his poor cousin Marionetta, said by herself and others to be simple though she speaks and acts quite cleverly; and the learned, sable-eyed beauty Stella, who enters the scene with an air of spectral mystery. This material is wittily handled and yields fun surprises, though without pretensions to—to anything, really, but certainly not to the psychological depth and observational precision with which Austen contemporaneously treated courtship and class. Peacock is chiefly interested in skewering the ennui, supernaturalism, abstraction, and Germanicism dominating the literary in-crowd, ridiculing if not exorcising the blue devils that, as Byron had it in *Childe Harold's Pilgrimage,* sought their prey:

> In melancholy bosoms, such as were
> Of moody texture from their earliest day
> And loved to dwell in darkness and dismay,
> Deeming themselves predestined to a doom
> Which is not of the pangs that pass away;
> Making the sun like blood, the earth a tomb,
> The tomb a hell, and hell itself a murkier gloom.

The stand-in for Coleridge, Mr. Flosky, is a poet of ceaseless vanity and a Kantian philosopher of dubious insight who stops in midsentence when he finds himself "unintentionally trespassing within the limits of common sense." A gross exaggeration, of course, though one that will likely find sympathizers in readers who've struggled through the more self-proud or recondite sections of *Biographia Literaria.* The Byron figure, Mr. Cypress, arrives relatively late in the book and isn't given Byronic charisma. Robert Southey takes offstage hits as Roderick Sackbut. Other characters either represent historical figures unremembered by nonscholars or are invented, such as odd-man-out Mr. Hilary, who by and large speaks for the author, though as Gore Vidal wrote in an essay on Peacock and the novel of ideas, Peacock "possessed negative capability to a high degree," and we can trust that even here he spread his own views among his disputants.

Nightmare Abbey is a delightfully hybrid book. Sometimes rendered in elegant novelistic prose, sometimes laid out like a play, it draws on Platonic and other philosophical dialogues, dialogic novels such as Diderot's *Rameau's Nephew,* as well as romances and farce, Rabelais and Voltaire. There are erudite debates, rakish French valets, original poems and songs, and slapstick tumbles into moats. Though not all the jokes have reached the twenty-first century in full luster, there are many sturdily inspired comic passages, including a precise and extended description of Scythrop settling into a pensive posture (". . . crossed his left foot over his right knee, placed the hollow of his left hand on the interior ancle of his left leg, rested his right elbow on the elbow of the chair . . . ,") that should appeal to fans of David Foster Wallace.

Peacock's references and allusions won't always leap to the current reader's mind (the book's two instances of anti-Semitism, alas, will be clear), but his satire is unusually durable, both because the romantics are still widely read, and because romanticism has informed so many subsequent artistic and intellectual vanguards. When one of the characters, Mr. Listless, finds in modern books a "consolatory and congenial" blight, "a delicious misanthropy and discontent, that demonstrates the nullity of virtue and energy, and puts me in good humour with myself and my sofa," one will perhaps be brought back to a youth of coffeehouse existentialism, or of Joy Division buttons, or whatever your age provides you. In times of personal despair or political fury, nothing can seem as insufferably bourgeois as happiness, but the artistic impulse to continually paint the world in somber tones, pursued either out of habit or in a sweating grasp for profundity, almost always misrepresents experience, obeying the silly first principle, as Mr. Hilary puts it, "to remember to forget that there are any such things as sunshine and music in the world." Or any such things as Thomas Love Peacock's strange little novels. ❧

Mr. Gates Goes to Washington

Stephen Hitchcock

I sometimes wonder what I am thinking. What I actually think. For example, when I recently said, "Honestly, I've been a bit surprised that the climate talks historically haven't had R&D on the agenda, in any way, shape or form," I wasn't being honest. At least not with myself. But then again who is? And how could we be? I'm rich. Filthy rich, people like to say. What do they know about how rich I am when they don't know how to be rich. It's not easy. Honestly. My money actually affects the weather. Makes climate change. What does yours do? Why did they take so long to ask me to join the talks? I was surprised at how hurt I was when I began to think about it. When I say think I think I mean feel. That's just it, I mostly don't know how I am feeling, what I honestly think. But I know what you're thinking. And I can see how you feel. America, I can see it: the way, the shape, the form. ॐ

Honest Mistake

Edward Mayes

While we had thought it odd to quibble
Over something as un-dire as place
Settings or to cavil about who saw who

And what and when and where and why,
We continued to surrender to *heavy*
Hors d'œuvre (horderves) we were told

To expect, and we were reminded
That sometime ago our aitches started
Dropping when other of our aitches

Became more attached, or when we
Have to turn the page this way
To properly read George Herbert's

"Easter Wings," the table full of
Canapés and antipasti, the H-bomb
Or was it the A-bomb dropped before

All of us were truly born, while few
Of us have packed corn on a fishhook
In hopes of carp rising out of the rivers,

For we had once honor, honor among
Hoodlums even, those of us who can't
Feign death anymore, or who prefer

The cleanliness of the fishing lure, or
To be done with failure finally, only
A few family members at the curtain call,

Schadenfreude filling the choir stalls, be it

All that keeps us humble, in aprons,
Ironing out the problems of Yalta—

Still—seventy years after the sit-down,
Leaders picking over the main course,
The pigs in blankets cooling beside

The baba ghanoush, and then of course
The final round—a thousand sorties for
The fire bombing—now, again, or at that hour.

Notes: Apoplexy; schlep, schlock jock; unlock; apart from the main course;
aperitifs; attic fan; hit don't matter; aitch dropping; hour, heir, hotel, historic;
great vowel shift; sac fly; foal, vole; fey, forget, forever; Yalta, Chekhov, Tolstoy;
iron curtain, it's curtains, curtail; mother board, ironing board

A Short Talk on the Afterlife

Edward Mayes

Done—as if what we did to infinity we thought
We could take back, the ice floe on the Mississippi
River, March, three deer, and if we really had

A place to jump to, how we embraced syllables even
Before we knew about letters, how we embraced
What we didn't know was arcane, but it *was*

Arcane, the first taste of Lapsang Souchong circa
1967, followed by oblivion, the iron left on on
The ironing board, shirts still sprinkled and

Rolled up, or the baseball we threw through
The basement window, or the train strike
At Tiburtina that left all of us on the platform,

Prolegomenon to the future of heaven,
The furrow we left unplanted and by then
It was too late, crates of chickens on the semi

We're behind in the taxi from Florence, the shall
We go with the shiplap or shall we go with the tongue
And groove dilemma, of not unrecent origin,

Although definitely postlapsarian, when we're
Left aching for abridgement, brumal times, we
Get longer and they get shorter, and then the vice

Versa, the brassard we wore for the Chicago 7
Trial circa 1969, or what we didn't remember eating
That day, *brevima dies* upon us, when we wanted

So much just to throw open the curtains to

See light, the few tickets left for the Brumalia,
And here we are, time-lapsing with anyone left.

*Notes: Burning abridgements; total collapse, bitchslap, burlap, earflaps;
abbreviation, amphibrach, embrace; shortest day; hops; clinical tribulations;
rabbet; lapsed cathode; river rats; the Brumalia festival before the Saturnalia
festival*

A Visit to the Antipodes

Carolyn Ferrell

Years ago, I assigned all three volumes of New Zealand writer Janet Frame's autobiography (*To the Is-Land, An Angel At My Table,* and *An Envoy From Mirror City*) to a graduate fiction workshop. The omnibus edition contained, in my eyes, every bit of instruction a writer could ever need; Frame's story was complete with melodrama, intrigue, violence, poverty, suffering, redemption, love, venom, and wild flights of imagination. Though the autobiography ends when she is in her thirties, its scope is large, often mind-boggling. What was not to like, I thought, as I watched the students sigh over the massive book and its author photo, right on the front cover—Janet Frame smiling cheerfully in front of a typewriter. Her life was anything but cheerful, but her observations, full of wit and poignancy, made the book (I thought) a compelling, welcoming read. The book is peppered with insights that would surely sway any skeptic: "The process of writing . . . may be set down . . . as laying a main trunk railway line from Then to Now, with branch excursions into the outlying wilderness." She ingeniously addressed the process of transforming lived experience into fiction, using a visit to Ibiza toward the end of the book as a launch point:

> As I sat at my table typing, I looked each day at the city mirrored in the sea, and one day I walked around the harbor road to the opposite shore where the real city lay that I knew only as the city in the sea, but I felt as if I were trying to walk behind a mirror, and I knew that whatever the outward phenomenon of light, city and sea, the real mirror city lay within as the city of the imagination . . .

Mirror City, in other words, was where a writer went to transform her life into art. This was something that would speak to my students, I thought; indeed—I also made these obedient people watch Jane Campion's masterful miniseries based on the autobiography (made for New Zealand TV), and I assigned excerpts from Frame's fiction, including her novel *Faces in the Water* and several stories from her (literally lifesaving) story collection, *The Lagoon.*

I assigned the students several chapters each week, leaving time in workshop to discuss Frame's process and then discuss student stories as well. There didn't seem to be an overt connection between Frame's literature and their own; and yet, the students seemed impressed with the power that lay in Frame's highly observant and meticulous eye ("How did she remember how many pleats her teacher's skirt had?" someone asked). The students plugged away at the tome, inspired by the storytelling and wisdom on nearly every page, and yet sagging under the weight of the reading—"Isn't this a writing workshop?" another asked during the first weeks of workshop, annoyed at my enthusiasm. Yes, sure it was, I answered—but whom better to learn from than the actual writers themselves? Of course, I was counting on the students to also fall under Frame's spell. But Frame's story was often emotionally draining—a pivotal moment in her autobiography occurs when she, as a young woman, is institutionalized at the behest of her parents (she was falsely diagnosed with schizophrenia) and eventually liberated from the mental hospital. A doctor recognizes her as a prizewinning author of *The Lagoon* (as a patient, Frame hadn't known her collection had even been published) and spares her from a lobotomy.

Towards mid-semester, I admitted Frame overload. Yes, there were lots of pages to take in, plenty to underline, making total progress through the autobiography unlikely. In graduate school I had a literature professor who would assign at least five books a week. I was not that professor, and yet . . . I was probably too far under Frame's spell to teach otherwise. The truth is, I have never stopped returning to her books. She reminds me why I could never be a good memoirist—real life, I have always told my fiction students, can be our enemy. Real life for me is always a launching pad, not the end product. Real life is shapeless (a lot of the time) and can take a long, long time to decipher. Frame wrote that "putting it all down as it happens is not fiction; there must be the journey by oneself, the changing of the light focused upon the material, the willingness of the author herself to live within that light . . . the real shape, the first shape, is always a circle formed, only to be broken and reformed again and again." And a bit later on in the autobiography: "So what have I seen in memory? Memory is not history. The passing of time does not flow like a ribbon held in the hand while the dancer remains momentarily still. Memory becomes scenes only until the past is not even yesterday, it is a series of retained moments released at random . . ."

I find I can never quite finish or even start a memoir. My memories work best as seeds for stories, where I don't have a straight line to follow, or where I can get at the emotional center without worrying about if I'm hewing closely to the "truth." Interestingly, Frame doesn't spend a lot of time in her autobiography on her time in the mental hospital, which is arguably one of the most dramatic and painful parts of the book; those details, however, are given powerful expression in *Faces in the Water.* Frame writes of the disappointment, upon first seeing a copy of *The Lagoon*, that there was no author photo in it; "I felt I had no claim to the book," she adds, "This, combined with my erasure in the hospital, seemed to set me too readily among the dead . . . my years between twenty and nearing thirty having passed unrecorded as if I had never been." In *Faces*, she saves her narrator from erasure, from stereotypical categorization:

> I wept and wondered and dreamed the abiding dream of most mental patients—The World—Outside, Freedom; and foretasted too vividly the occasions I most feared—electric shock treatment, being shut in a single room, being sent to Ward Two, the disturbed ward. I dreamed of the world because it seemed the accepted thing to do, because I could not bear to face the thought that not all prisoners dream of freedom...

Her story "The Bedjacket" is a gem in *The Lagoon*. In it, the narrator tells the story of Nan, a seemingly model patient who has formed a relationship with Nurse Harper, an unusually kind person; Nan lives vicariously through her, not wanting to leave the hospital at all (as the other patients want to do). Nan decides to knit a bedjacket as a Christmas gift, and slowly suffers a meltdown:

> "'I've never knitted before,' she said. 'And now I've made it I don't want to give it away, because it's mine, I made it. It belongs to me. Nothing's ever belonged to me before. I made it. It belongs to me'... That night [they] took Nan out of the ward and down to a single room where she wouldn't disturb the other patients. For four days she was by herself... she held the bedjacket under her arm, and she stroked it and fondled it as if it were a live thing."

Frame gets at Nan's desperation, at her frailty, her desire to remain connected in some way to the world outside and her realization that that can't happen.

Frame was a master at defamiliarization; worlds of feeling and action are contained in her most ordinary, unassuming moments, our assumptions are challenged, our story knowledge tested. What makes fiction live and breathe? Frame understood "the only certainty about writing and trying to be a writer is that it has to be done, not dreamed of or planned and never written, or talked about (the ego eventually falls apart like a soaked sponge) but simply written: it's a dreary awful fact that writing is like any other work..."

It would be, in Frame's eyes, a mistake to see her life simply transferred to the page without having traveled its journey to the place she called "Mirror City," that place where people and events and memories are transformed by the creative process. They cease being mere "slices of life." Her time away from New Zealand helped make her a "citizen of the Mirror City"—the place, as she puts it so beautifully, where "nothing is without its use," where "memories are resurrected, reclothed with reflection and change, and their essence [left] untouched."

For a poem to coalesce, Adrienne Rich said:

> . . . a character or an action to take shape, there has to be an imaginative transformation of reality which is in no way passive. And a certain freedom of the mind is needed. . .[if] the imagination is to transcend and transform experience, it has to question, to challenge, to conceive of alternatives, perhaps to the very life you are living at that moment. You have to be free to play around with the notion that day might be night, love might be hate; nothing can be too sacred for the imagination to turn into its opposite or to call experimentally by another name. For writing is renaming."

This is what I wanted my students to gain from their reading of Frame's fiction and non-fiction: the ability to take life's events and fictionalize them with power and clarity, as well as the capacity to transform the imagination's events, imbuing them with the most deeply felt life on the page. To take life's events and fictionalize them with power and clarity, but taking the imagination's events and giving them the most deeply felt life on the page: this is what I wanted my students to take from reading Frame's fiction and non-fiction. Yes, it was a lot of work. But for us writers, when will it *not* be a lot of work? ❧

Hang It on the Limb

Colin Fleming

After my career rimrocked and my wife left me for my brother, I spent the majority of the last three years of my thirties getting drunk starting at five in the afternoon, ceding the final few of those one thousand days to becoming sober and falling in love with a twenty-two-year old violinist who quoted Tolstoy and whose first words to me were, "I am Rebecca Buford-Hayes, and I fuck."

Getting rimrocked is what happens when you're hiking and you descend a ledge and find yourself on an outcrop of stone from which you can't go down, and you can't get back up to from where you came. I was stupid enough to try and earn my bread and cheese by writing alone, which meant sending out twenty thousand words' worth of pitches a week so I could get someone to pay me $250 to write on Cubist sculpture one day, someone else $100 to write on P.G. Wodehouse the next.

This meant coming around a lot, and when you come around a lot, people get sick of you, and you find yourself on that outcrop. My wife leaving with my brother was no real surprise, because we both knew that one of us—and probably her, because I was too much of a romantic loyalist—would be setting off with someone, and our marriage was such that after a point we were just marking time. My brother and I didn't have any closeness, or any ire for each other. I think he probably thought I thought of it as a favor to get my ass in gear with the next phase of my life. My brother is also kind of an idiot.

I was living in Danbury, Connecticut, in the shadow of the Danbury Fair Mall, which is notable simply because there's this big carousel in it, and some days I'd bring my laptop, get a fish sandwich in the food courtyard, and sit in the same carousel booth with carved, buttery-pink pigs on each side, and go round and round, dicking about with online dating sites. And that's how I met Rebecca. Or, as I called her, Bex.

She was a student at Oberlin, the school's violin concertmaster and a creative writing major, with some risque photos at the top of her profile I might have found titillating, had my focus not been centered on the scared looking creature who seemed so out of her element at the center of them.

My eyes moved to hers, which even in a blurry photo appeared to move and scan about. But then again, there she was in a bikini in one shot by some sickly looking creek, lying down in her underwear with her ass in the air in another, and this being a dating site, I figured maybe I'd be what for me was flirty and call some attention to this, but with a periodic sentence or two mixed in.

She wrote of sex and how freely she had it, but also of Russian literature, and there were words like "disconsolate," "peripatetic," and "nonplussed." While I had maybe not learned a ton in this world up until that point, I knew that it was about once every two or three years I met someone who truly interested me, who got me to think and feel and buzz alive with emotion and knowledge, and when I did, I didn't care if they were seventy or twenty.

I sent some lame note asking who she was and what she did, besides exhibiting a disdain for clothes when in the proximity of addled streams, and I got the "I fuck" line. Which was amended with "I also write, I read deep into the night when everyone is asleep, I wonder what greater purpose I can find in my life, and I fight to be less alone, often with others, but more painfully with myself. What is it you do?"

I get gobsmacked by a girl like this, apparently, is what I do.

Our first phone conversation lasted for eleven hours, and I had never felt adrenaline pump through me like that. We'd go from talking about the architecture of bridges to Bach cantatas to how we both loved the *Rudolph* Animagic Christmas special, that 1960s one, and how she was coming east, to Greenwich, to study with some violin master over the January break. And so she did, and it was like the universe was giving us a little push together.

She'd take her lessons in the morning, and then I'd drive out to those mannered streets, pick her up, and we'd spend the day at my rat's nest of an apartment, where I'd write, she'd play, and we'd lose ourselves in ourselves for hours in the bed.

And then she'd go quiet for hours, sometimes while I held her, and cry as quietly as I imagine it is possible to cry, and I would look into eyes that, even as they radiated so much life, appeared so cold, like something you'd pop out and stick on a snowman you'd made when you were a kid, eyes replete with that special make of sadness that never gains expression in words, but only in the expression cast back by the person who loves that particular individual.

"Do you know what my favorite part in *Rudolph* is?" she asked me after she had just defeated me in our first ever game of all-naked Battleship.

"When the snowman Burl Ives guy does the 'have a holly jolly Christmas' bit?"

"No, Oliver. It's at the start, when Rudolph is asking out the girl reindeer Clarice after everyone has made fun of him, and she says, 'I'll walk with you.' And what that means. Someone to walk with you. 'Take my hand and walk with me.' I don't know if there's anything rarer than really walking with someone. That kind of walking."

She was the only person who called me Oliver. To everyone else I was Olly. Not the same spelling as Ollie Hardy, from Laurel and Hardy, so I was almost always mis-billed as Ollie Redgole in the articles I published. But I liked that Bex—and I always called her Bex, because she said no one else did—called me something no one else did because I knew we weren't like anyone else. And Bex and Oliver, Oliver and Bex, had a oneness for me, a blendedness sans seams. This is a horrible way of putting it, but a frothing gash in her arm would have no more grossed me out than one in mine. And I had never felt that way before.

I was on assignment up in Boston for a Red Sox story when it came time for Bex to go back to Oberlin. She asked to meet my mother, who lived in Enfield, so a meeting was brokered in a tea room that used to be a HoJo's. My sister had died of a heroin overdose that past summer, and with that and the whole brother-taking-other-brother's-wife fiasco, we were pretty Addams Family at that point.

Knowing my mom, it didn't surprise me to learn, later, that she asked Bex not to hurt her son. Nor did it shock me, exactly, to learn that before that, Bex had sat in front of her, over their scones, and said, calmly, but with those eyes leaping about in their way of hers, that she loved her son. There was a reference to really walking with someone, and hands being taken, which my mother did not understand, but I did.

Three days later, Bex was back at Oberlin, I had booked my first trip out there for three weeks hence, the Red Sox piece was filed, and I was replaying a voicemail that said, "I am sorry, so sorry, so sorry, but I just can't do this, I can't do this with us."

I had a bottle of Ardbeg in the kitchen. I left the bottle of Ardbeg in the kitchen. And I wrote. For most of a month. I just was so certain. I had no exact reasons to be so certain. But that's when you tend to know the most. Which is what my late father would have called the bitch of it.

"What's the 'it' refer to?" I asked him the first time he said his line, which he repurposed frequently.

"Why, life, of course."

He had a point there.

When some aspect of my life goes belly-up, I write. It's what I've done since I was in third grade and maybe kickball hadn't worked out as I had hoped at recess, and I wrote Bex every day, without response. I didn't feel like a doormat, though I understand how I looked like one. But if I believe in something, I'll go for it, appearances be damned.

She finally replied after a week and a half with a letter replete with rococo young person laments interwoven amongst the news of how she spent her mornings drinking, sometimes passing out as her forearms bled from cutting herself, hoping she wouldn't wake up.

No one knew, she said. Not her friends, no one in her Durham-based family, including her psychiatrist mother who worked at Duke treating PTSD war vets, nor her father, whom I had reason to know of.

He was powerful enough in the world of fiction that his name, Clifton Hayes, did not feature on anyone's masthead, but if you were in the business deep enough, as even a rimrocker like myself was, you knew he harvested a lot of the stories that featured in the high circulation venues. He was rumored to be capricious to the point of rejecting a Pulitzer winner's story because of the thickness of the paper it came in on, and prone to intense editorial tête-à-têtes that left ostensibly unflappable writers reduced to slobbering messes who couldn't function for a couple weeks.

But I didn't care about that. I saw someone who needed help, whom I thought I knew better than other people did. She wrote that being with me was like having your feet bound and then let free, and the freedom was too much, the light I gave too bright—she tended to mix her metaphors—our prospective joint exponential curve too limitless, so that she needed the twine to cut back into flesh again, because that's what she knew.

Silence resumed until she phoned me in the middle of the night, and said all she needed to say to get me to depart, as I was scheduled to, for Cleveland.

"Oliver."

"Hey, Bex."

"Will you . . ."

"Yeah."

"Take a . . ."

"You know I will."

She had housemates who wanted no part of someone my age staying with them, even if I could pass for twenty-five back then. I took up residence in a motel called The Berm, named, I suppose, because of its sloped roof.

She told me she'd done something with her birth control pill to make sure she was menstruating when I was there, and we were like something out of a D.H. Lawrence novel, taking our physical connection back to a time when that portion of the country was nothing but grassy rolling fields and the beasts copulating in them, but with our ever-burgeoning streak of tenderness cutting through the caked on dirt.

We raced around to a concert of Chopin nocturnes, to the art museum, to the library, where we'd pull down books and show each other our favorite passages before reaching for each other in a dimly-lit alcove.

After a few days, the bed sheet back at The Berm—for she had asked that the maid not change it—looked like a Motherwell canvas, but we'd sit atop it and watch films on her computer, like my favorite, *Scrooge* from 1951, which caused her to laugh in parts that had taken me several screenings to get, and a relic called *I Am a Fugitive From a Chain Gang* from 1932 that she really liked.

Paul Muni's character is wrongfully convicted, ends up breaking rocks on that aforesaid chain gang, can't get free, that kind of movie. But her favorite thing was what someone would say when they were going to do something legitimately brave, like make a burst for freedom as the bullets were about to fly.

"What are you going do?" an old convict would ask Muni, and Muni, mentally calculating the dim chances of escape, would nonetheless respond with, "I think I'm going to hang it on the limb." Then he'd make his break for it, bang bang, pop pop.

We started saying it to each other. At this awful bar adjoined to The Berm that had all of six stools in it, over warm beers, she asked me what I felt about marriage, and in thirty seconds time it was a case of "should we hang it on the limb?" You can be engaged for years, I figured, and I knew this was the person I wanted to be with. So we agreed. Done deal.

I was supposed to go back to Connecticut the following morning, and she was heading to Durham for a long weekend. But I didn't leave The Berm for another few days as I holed up in my t-shirt and boxers, agonizing over what to do next. She had texted me from the airport in North Carolina. She was really there, she said, for a battery of tests with a team of mental health providers assembled by her mother. She felt like she was barely hanging on. She had need of the binding. That's how she put it. But she believed, ultimately, we'd always be together. Maybe starting in five years. Maybe ten. But at some point.

I wanted to feel differently than I did about her, but I didn't. Like I said, you just know. That doesn't mean it works out. You can have the best team in the league and if the manager shoots every player in the ass, you're not taking the pennant.

I decided to do what that guy on the lam in the old TV show *The Fugitive* does and head out West, doing odd jobs to pay for my keep as I went, hopefully making my way to Alaska, where I wanted to find work crab fishing, as that seemed the closest you could get to a dangerous job like whaling in the twenty-first century, and I aimed to pull a Melville and light out.

I wasn't an easy man to find, with my increasingly scattershot jobs, like working on controlled burns, but Bex's parents tracked me down with a letter in Normal, Illinois, where I was bartending at a jazz club. Rebecca had kept a journal, they said. I was the focus of a lot of it. They wanted me to come and talk at a ceremony they wished to give for her, because "she is no longer with us and our daughter loved you."

Full stop.

I cried like you cry when you feel like you won't get to die if you don't, and you want to expire then and there, so you howl.

And then I made like Robert Johnson and caught a Greyhound bus—well, Peter Pan, anyway—and rode.

I was in Durham by the middle of the next day, thinking how well the overly-bright flowers of the North Carolina spring could function as set dressing for the hell playing out in my mind.

I started off back in another motel, The High Flyer, with a distinct nautical theme—fishing nets were tacked up everywhere—despite being miles from the coast. I had some notes I had written out to present to Bex's parents, as I figured they'd want to vet what I had to say. I called a cab and made my way to the yellow Georgian house that this person whom I loved, whom I'd never know again, grew up in. The woman I assumed was the cleaning lady—she was Latino, wearing sweats, and toting a vacuum around—let me in, and pointed to a study that had a strangely narrow door, like you'd have to turn sideways to get through it without grazing anything. I did just that, and entered a huge room that must have held a couple thousand books in shelf after shelf that went to the ceiling. The room flowed into another, where there were more books, and Bex's parents waiting for me.

Her mother was mousy, like those people I'd met at the few publishing conferences I had ever gone to. She thanked me for coming without looking me in the eye, and her handshake was so light as to make you think you were making the acquaintance of a spirit.

Clifton Buford was short, but he looked maybe thirty, though he must have been in his late forties. He was absolutely ripped with muscles, with this Charles Atlas look going on, and it seemed like he'd be more comfortable in a loin cloth with some barbells at his side than the suit he was wearing.

"I know your work well. There are opportunities for someone like you. I've read you for years. You command prose well."

I was a little taken aback.

"That's . . . wow . . . I mean, thanks. I didn't think anyone . . . I figured no one reads any of it. Just a paycheck, you know?"

As I looked around the room, they did, too, with that paycheck line hanging in the air. They were somber but not sad—austere, I'd say, rather than engulfed in grief. He appeared to want to get down to business, and his wife simply looked like she wished to be alone. Maybe reading, maybe shopping. But not here. I decided to hasten everything along and take the lead. I don't know why. I wasn't nervous. But I missed Bex, and being here made me want to learn things about her I never got to—what her first job was, if she was scared her first day of middle school, what was her favorite Christmas—such that I wanted to leave, and I wanted to take a drink, a lot of drinks. Or write, anyway.

I pulled out my little speech from my pocket, said something about here's what I've prepared, and the look in their faces told me that this wasn't for some funeral or anything. He put his hand on my shoulder in this sort of forced way, like when you're trying to make a point and you want an additional human component, and said they wanted my recollections of their daughter. Nothing more.

You can be way wrong, of course, but sometimes you have this overpowering sense that something is up, and I had that feeling now. I was about to say that I was confused, I was under the impression that such and such had happened, and I felt my heart all but roll in my chest, as a girl entered the room, from back where the narrow door was. For a second I thought she was Bex— she was also six foot tall, same light red hair, like it was flecked with sand and traces of thinly sliced garnet, and also didn't shave under her arms—save that the eyes were different.

These were of a darker color than Bex's hazel, more of a deep walnut shade, but they moved with the same celerity, and even as my heart pounded, my mind at least was able to step into the breach and flash out to me, as though utilizing Morse code, that this was Emily, Bex's older sister by fifteen months, a musician as well. A flautist, to be precise.

I must have looked a mess, because Clifton stood up at that point and stuck his hand out, a sure dismissal, and Emily put her head down and shook it, barely, but shook it still, one of those head shakes that are the visual representation of a sigh. I said my thanks yous, wished them all the best, and fled—there's no other word for it—back to The High Flyer.

I was sitting in my room three hours later, still freaking out, heart-broken and confused, trying to calm myself by doing a Google search on just what the hell a high flyer was—the buoy part of a lobster trap, as it turns out—when someone knocked at the door, and I reprised the heart roll bit, as Emily asked if she could come in, after I had again mistaken her for Bex.

And that is how that started.

I stayed at The High Flyer for a month and a half. At first, Emily would come by, and we'd just talk. Never about Bex.

She was calmer, more of an assuring presence, but she always had a thermos on her that was filled with her dad's Balvenie Doublewood Scotch. I wondered if that accounted for her placidity, or if it was something she turned to with her sister being gone. And, I confess, I felt like I was keeping something going that didn't exist anymore. When you want a relationship so bad, and there's no way you can have it, you can fall into the trap of taking the most tenuous variation of what remains, and I was doing that. At the same time, I felt at my ease with this person, and I was not someone, in a long time, who had known any amount of ease.

She'd play for me, and she was good enough that it could have been her career, but it wasn't, she said, what she wanted to do.

"Well, what then?"

"I write poems."

"I know you write poems. I read thirty of them last night that you'd given me."

"I didn't say I wanted to be a poet. Can you even be a poet?"

"Can't really be your job."

"I don't want to be here. There's that. Not here with you, I don't mean. I guess what I want is to contribute to something that makes me bigger than I am on my own, but which would always be a lot bigger than me in anything else I might do. It's like when you're a kid, and another kid tells you if you go out in the backyard and keep digging, you can make it all the way to the center of the earth. There's no logical reason you can't, you think, when you're a kid, but you're scared that maybe you'll get too ambitious, too effective, too committed to that cause, that you'll get to the center of the earth and it will come out and overrun things and that won't be good for anyone, or else the center of the earth will swallow you up, and you'll lose yourself. But I want to find something that swallows me up in a good way and that's how I find myself and everything I might be."

She'd talk like that, after a few weeks, when I was inside of her, not having left town and made The High Flyer my base of operations as I got back to writing professionally. I guess someone might say this was all pretty necromantic on my part, but after our first few times hanging out, which meant grabbing coffee at a Starbucks, and then taking a trip to hike the Appalachians, which I knew Bex had loved, Emily didn't feel like anyone but Emily, even if she looked like someone I had been certain I was going to be with. The first time she undressed in front of me I was relieved to see that her pubic hair grew to her thighs, unlike Bex, who didn't have any save a tuft atop her labia. She didn't cut herself, but she drank more than I would have believed possible without passing out, and it didn't even alter her speech. She drove, too, after drinking like that, despite me begging her not to.

"It doesn't affect me," she'd say.

"Then why do it?" I'd counter.

"Because this is here, and I'm not somewhere else. Now hold me, Olly."

I would, and she wouldn't cry like Bex did, and even though emotions lit up her eyes as if tropical storms were playing out inside of them, I never saw her cry. Save for me. Because at night, I'd sometimes get up and go to the window and I'd wonder what the hell I was doing, and why I was okay with it feeling so okay when I had known with certainty, just a few months before, who my person, so to speak, was, and now here I was, and I was no less certain that I had everything correctly figured out before, and this person was not that person, but rather the instigator of different feelings that were less extreme and galvanic, maybe, but which fluttered through me more broadly, and didn't so much speak to what was, as to what would be. An unfurling. And I'd never been an unfurling kind of guy. I wasn't good at letting processes play out.

I had an assignment that took me up to Harvard to do a piece on film conservation techniques at the Brattle Theatre. Emily was supposed to come back for our last night before I left, but she didn't show, which was not at all like her. I didn't want to nag, but she was someone—and how could I not, after everything—I worried about and for whom I wished I could make my arm turn into some giant protective curtain I could put around her to shield her from anything that might cause pain, so I asked, over a text, if she was okay, and got back: "Yes, have a good trip, be safe, talk when you get back, Love E."

You'd think I was going on safari rather than to Harvard Square. I was only supposed to be in Boston for that weekend, but there was flooding at the Brattle, and that meant my stay got extended over a week as I waited on the conservation people to clean up everything.

I killed time as I always liked to in Boston by going to the symphony. One of my favorite things in Sherlock Holmes stories is how Holmes would always delight in drifting off to what he called violin land, and I had always been the same. I recall noting that it was strange, maybe, that I could go to a Handel and Haydn Society performance of Bach's St. Matthew Passion after everything with Bex, but I kept reminding myself I'd done nothing wrong, and no matter how much you care about someone, no matter what you'd do for them, nothing stops life from going on, and life doesn't get delayed by what you might be going through. You have to start marching again in time to it. Or you'll get trampled.

That's the rhetoric I was plying myself with as I sat in Symphony Hall, and my eye caught the eye of a back row violinist who made me think my imagination was doing that same thing it did after my wife left with my brother, when I'd go to some spot I didn't normally go to, and think I had just seen her leaving as I came in. I was crossing a bridge over the Mystic River one time and I could have sworn I saw her going the other way, such that I turned around and followed an individual who was just some random, similarly tall woman who looked terrified as I came upon her all wide-eyed, expecting to see my wife.

I tried to banish the thought from my head, but I kept attending performances over that week, and after the fourth one, there was no way I was not going backstage following the final round of applause, even if I had to force my way in.

I didn't have to. You just had to go through a door that said an alarm would sound—one didn't—and up a few stairs, and I knew, by then, what I'd find. I knew it'd be her. I knew because I guess I knew her. I knew her as someone I loved who wasn't as alive as she wanted to be. And I know when you're not as alive as you want to be, maybe you rig things so that you can get that infusion of life you need, or maybe you dig to the center of the earth and hope you get to be what you have it in you to be because you had the courage to get swallowed up by something.

"Does Emily know?" was the first thing I asked as she stood in front of me, violin bow in hand, shaking, and starting to cry.

"Emily knows. Everyone knows. I wanted to write something."

"You wanted to write something? What the fuck does that mean?"

"Something good. And something to you. I knew you wouldn't come if it were anything else. And I knew I couldn't be with you. And I wanted to know if you'd come. Because I thought some time, at some point, later . . . and my family is fucked up as it is, and they were worried about me, and my dad kind of knew you and knew how we were . . . "

"What the motherfuck? Who does this?"

"Is it love?"

"You knew how I felt. The whole take a walk deal. You knew exactly how I felt. You knew there wasn't anything I wouldn't have done. Nothing I wouldn't have given up. But what is this, like some fucking Hitchcock shit?"

"No, I mean Emily. Do you love Emily?"

"I am not doing this insanity with you."

She shook more, and tried to contain it, which made me think she was going to crack from the inside out and fall to dust at my feet, and, fuck me, I didn't want that.

"She didn't say anything to me."

"It wasn't her place. She thought I was going to see you, and then I left, I came back here, and . . . I guess it was like I was dead. No one has ever made me feel not dead, Oliver. Nothing ever has. I need your help. Please."

She put her two hands over one of mine, and I didn't pull it back. I felt like I was out of my own body, hovering overhead, wondering what that fellow down there might do.

"I need your help. I know this is fucked. I know this is so wrong. But you know me. You know what we had, our exponential curve. You know that was real. You know I was it. I'm not some monster. I need help. I need your help. Please, Oliver."

I believed her. Because I knew her. I knew what she was, I knew what she was to me. I knew that she could do something this fucked up without being the gorgon that someone else, surely, would have told me she had to have been. I knew there were worlds in her, more worlds than most people, and when there are more worlds, more of them can collide, more can go wrong. But I still knew what I had to do at that moment. I fled.

I walked twenty miles that night around Boston and Cambridge, and then I sat on a bridge over the Charles where there was this plaque some Harvard students had placed in the ground to mark where Faulkner's

Quentin Compson took his leap into the river. She texted me as I sat there, and told me where she was, at an apartment in Allston. She told me she needed me. Please. I need you to come. Please.

I did. She opened the door naked. I could make out tracks from tears down her neck, all the way to her breasts. She leaned into me, in the doorway, and put her forehead against mine, and our eyes moved downwards together. I saw that red tuft of pubic hair in the half-light, I felt her breathing, I felt my breath adjusting to the rhythms of her own, and I felt my own tears start to gather and release and roll down my cheeks, as hers did. I told her I loved her. And I told her I had to go.

Emily was not awaiting my return at The High Flyer. I phoned and texted for a full day, and heard nothing. Bex had maybe called her.

The next morning, I thought, screw this, I'm going to the house. I rang the bell and waited for what seemed an age, ready to say whatever I had to say to Clifton or his mousy wife to see their daughter. Instead, the door was opened by the housekeeper again. I decided to ally myself with her.

"Hola."

"What?"

"It means 'hello.'"

"I know. Can I help you?"

"I want to see Emily."

"You not heard?"

"No. Nothing." I was nervous. Sometimes when I'm nervous I make grim jokes that no one could find funny. "I'm a broken man. I think. I don't know if my ears would even work. Sorry. I'm sorry. Where is she?"

"She was in an accident. Yesterday. Someone blindsided her. They kept her overnight in the hospital. For observation. She fine."

I wasn't. And I knew I had no right to involve this girl in my own struggles. Because I wondered, I wondered so hard it made me want to cut my brain out of my head, that if all things being equal I might have—

"Look, I know this is unusual. I need you to give her a message for me. From Olly. Tell her I do love her, but I'm awful at processes, and I don't know that I know where the middle of the earth is. I can write it down. That's a stupid message. Just remember the earth thing. She'll get the earth thing. Thank you. I'm sorry. I know this is weird. I have to go."

And with that, I hung it on the limb, not at all sure if I'd done so for the right reason, or because I was an idiot.

I chucked my phone, shut down my email, and eventually I began to get off that ledge I had been rimrocked on in my career. I had a video camera, and I'd go out to various outposts in the woods, in the desert, in the mountains, and I'd write about being there, in live time, talking as I did so, crafting some unique, I think, podcasts that not only got me noticed, but led to a site that got as much traffic as any in publishing, and book deals that proved, maybe, there was a point to what I had long ago set out to do after all.

I was off the grid, but not especially hard to find, if you really wanted to put some effort in, because you could just go on the site, see where I was, and make your way through Mother Nature to roll up on my latest temporary doorstep. Editors and publishers were my most common guests, but in later years, as everything built and built, and I had forsaken my wanderings for a house in Falmouth, in Cape Cod, writers doing profiles for magazines were more the norm.

I'd tell them about my travels, and how I came to write this piece or that one, and sometimes I'd work in a very skeletal version of this story, without much in the way of detail, but, I think, a goodly amount of emotion—for I cannot really withhold that in this instance—and I would talk about the people who visited me in places like the Pacific Rain Forest, or in the swamps of Florida, or the time a girl drove all the way out to the most remote point of Vermont, and then made her way on foot through woods where even few hunters ever went, just to see me.

The guys from the magazines that I shared that detail with would always look satisfied, like if they kept writing, they too could have comely, devoted visitors no matter where they went.

But the women writers, without fail, always have a different reaction to my anecdote about the girl, who was quite tall, who happened upon me as I crouched outside my tent in those woods where hunters rarely went, in my Christmas boxers and Bruins shirt, trying to clean a fish.

I don't say that you could tell who she was because she was carrying an instrument case, and its size gave her away, but it is at this point in our little profile interviews that the woman talking to me will turn to the other woman in the room, whom I had probably introduced previously simply as my wife, because there is now a solidity in that term I luxuriate in, and breathlessly ask, "What did you call him? What did you call him?"

You'd think a life depended on it.

I enjoy, and I suppose I'll always enjoy, watching how the walnut color of my wife's eyes seems to darken as she answers, to become richer, more something for you to be swallowed up in.

"I called him Olly, of course. Wouldn't you?" ❧

Suicide and Marrowfat Peas

Jason Stoneking

When Leslie and I got together, I was already accustomed to dipping in and out of homeless. I'd lived in parks and on beaches, I'd couch-surfed all over the country, I'd slept on the bus for hours as it traveled around town, and I'd thumbed long-distance rides and fallen asleep in strangers' cars. I was perfectly comfortable not worrying about where I was going to wind up sleeping on a given night. I knew that I could usually organize something; if it fell through I could always just scrape up some change for a refillable coffee at an all-night diner, or I could go read religious pamphlets at the bus station until the sun came up and I could crash on a park bench without getting rousted by the cops. But Leslie didn't have these fall-back habits in her arsenal. Before her relationship with me, she had always had a steady place to live. So when we started traveling together, and didn't always have plans for our sleeping accommodations, it tended to stress her out pretty badly. But she also started to fall for the lure of the road. And when we found ourselves getting stuck in a rut, working miserable jobs, it didn't take long for us both to get the itch again.

I suggested that we move back to Paris. That's where I had lived before I was with Leslie, and it was a place where I'd had a lot of luck slipping through the cracks. I had found some interesting people to hang out with, and lots of little ways to survive. I trusted Paris as a city that would always find a way to look after its dreamers. Leslie was game for the move, but she was a little more cautious than I was. We hardly had any money to leave with, maybe enough to get us through a few carefully managed months, and we only had a couple of shaky leads on places to crash. Leslie suggested that we just go over there for a few months, so that we'd have a ticket back if things didn't pan out. Even if she was tentative about my assertion that somehow everything would be fine if we could just get back to France, she was also sick enough of our hamster-wheel life in the States that she was willing to give it a go. We had pretty good luck on that first trip, finding temporary rooms and little gigs here and there to help pay for them. Leslie sold a few drawings and photos, while I played guitar in a few bars. Eventually her confidence increased and we decided to try for a more long-term relocation.

One of the great things we had going for us in Paris was the network of tiny little romantic apartments all over the city. They are generally referred to as *chambres de bonne*, or maids' quarters. Most of the older buildings in the city center have these small rooms, which at one time were the sleeping chambers for the domestic help employed by the residents of the larger homes. They are often located on the top floor, cut off by the slant of the roof, and generally under a hundred square feet in size. In fact, many of them are too small to be legally rented as living spaces under Parisian housing regulations, but this also makes them cheap. Unlike the housing in New York or London, where anything even remotely near the city center would cost thousands per month, these romantic little rooms, scattered throughout the very heart of Paris, can often be had for as little as a couple hundred. So there is a thriving black market through which they are rented, exchanged, and acquired. They are prized by artists, writers, and students as an affordable way for the less affluent among us to bed down in the City of Light. And because they are in such high demand, if you want to hear about them, you have to be plugged into the network of expats and starving artists who pass messages about these places along a hidden grapevine, like keepers of a secret handshake.

When Leslie and I came back to stay, we floated in and out of temporary residence in several of those little rooms around town, and we managed to get ourselves tied fairly well into that grapevine. But it still wasn't exactly easy to find a permanent home. We'd get one for two months here or three months there, but then we kept finding ourselves back on the streets or crashing for short times with friends. This instability used to terrify Leslie. She took it more literally than I did. I had learned from years of experience that first of all, something always comes along when you're in a jam, and second of all, that even when it doesn't, a night in the train station, or a day spent sleeping in the park, is never as bad as you abstractly fear that it will be. Leslie was starting to understand those things too, but the transitions would still put her on edge. In March of 2004, we were staying in a cheap hotel, down to our last few euros, and we were getting close to rejoining the homeless population. Leslie was getting nervous. So I proposed what I always thought, and what I still think, is appropriate to do in such a situation. I suggested that we go down to the pub, and start investing the meager remnants of our finances in some beer and conversation.

Leslie thought I was nuts wanting to waste both our precious time and our humble coins in an afternoon at the bar, but there was a method to my madness. When you're down on your luck, it's important to be visible. Especially in places where you're a regular and the familiarity of your face has accrued a bit of sympathy and good will. When things aren't working out is when you most need a favor, or the flash of inspiration that you might get from meeting someone new or overhearing a conversation. And you're not going to get that sitting in your room, counting your pennies. When you have a good-sized chunk of money it might be worth saving, but when you only have a few bucks, its greatest value is in the chair time it can buy you at the watering hole. I finally talked Leslie into it, partly because she didn't have any better ideas, and partly because I would have gone down there without her if I had to. We went to an old favorite bar on the rue Mouffetard, where I knew the owner from my younger days. Leslie and I had frequented the place before, and had reason to hope that we might run into an old friend, or meet a new one, or otherwise catch a lead on a place to crash. We went early, when the beers were cheapest, and got ourselves a couple of pints. Then we sat down at our usual end of the bar and got to work on the crossword puzzles in the English papers while we waited for some other regulars to pop their heads in and ask us how things were going.

The English crosswords always posed a bit of an extra challenge to us, being that they so often incorporated cultural references, spellings, and phrasings that were foreign to the American vocabulary. This day's puzzle was no exception. After solving the bulk of it, we got stuck on the long, two-word phrase running down the middle. We were confident about at least half of the letters, and they seemed to define the likely syllabic structure of some words, but the pattern didn't bring anything the least bit familiar to mind. Thankfully, our whining and grumbling was overheard by a young Irish language lover a few stools up the bar from us. This was the person who would go on to become our very dear friend Mark. He introduced himself and asked curiously what the trouble seemed to be. When we showed him the puzzle, he realized straight away that the answer we struggled so mightily to find was "marrowfat peas." Leslie and I had never even heard of marrowfat peas, so we were happy to be let off the hook by our new friend.

Not only did we hit it off quickly with Mark, but when the conversation moved on to what we were all doing in Paris, and we explained our predicament to him, his eyes flew wide in eureka recognition. He told us about how he had just met an American guy, in the preceding days, who'd been trying to rent out a cheap little room as quickly as possible. He cautioned us that he had passed on the room himself, due to some strange circumstances surrounding it, but suggested that if we were desperate it might be just the right fit. We assured him that we were, and that it was. So he offered to put us in touch with the guy and let him explain the unusual details to us himself. Mark called Anthony from the phone at the bar and told him he was with some people who might be up for renting the room. Then he handed me the phone. Anthony warned us that the place was tiny, but it was almost impossibly cheap. At 260 euros per month, we could almost find the rent just by looking for coins on the floor of the subway. He said he needed a renter as soon as possible, and I told him we'd take it (assuming I'd dig up the money somehow); he thought it might be a good idea if he came down to the bar first to describe the "complicated situation" in person. Unfazed, we told him we'd be happy to wait, and then we joyfully ordered up a celebratory pint with Mark.

When Anthony arrived, he explained that he had been subletting the apartment from a young German guy named Jan who had recently taken his own life. He said that Jan's parents had come through town to pick up his belongings and arrange a memorial, and that they had told him it was ok for him to keep renting the flat. But since then, he said, they had fallen out of touch. He had kept sending the rent to Jan's father for a while, but was no longer receiving a response. So Anthony, a college-age guy who was also on a tight budget, had found other sleeping arrangements for himself and decided to rent this place out. But he wanted us to know up front that Jan's parents might resurface at any time and expect us to move out of the place. We were fairly used to these kinds of temporary arrangements, and anything was better than our impending homelessness, so we thanked him for the opportunity and got to work looking for the rent. Our friend Chris, who was in a similar situation at the time but had a small amount of savings, joined up with us and helped with the expenses. Despite the unusual circumstances, we were all relieved to have found a place to crash for a while. But once we moved in, we began to feel a little bit haunted by the story of Jan.

Jan had been a troubled young man, and one day he had knocked on the door of a stranger, who lived on the top floor of one of the taller buildings in his neighborhood. When the woman who lived there had opened the door, he had calmly asked her, "May I use your apartment to kill myself?" When the slightly confused older lady didn't know how to respond, Jan had brushed past her, placed a single piece of paper on her table, crossed her living room to the balcony overlooking the street, and then walked straight off the balcony and fallen to his death below. The piece of paper Jan had left on the woman's table had read, "In Paris we live like dogs, when we should be living like kings." And here we were living in Paris, and living in Jan's apartment. Jan had been a creative soul, and we felt connected to his struggle, and felt honor-bound to try to get to know this mythical German martyr through the handful of artifacts he had left behind: some homemade cassette recordings of jazz and classical music from the radio, some old black and white tourist photos printed on thick cards, a cracked chess board with no accompanying pieces, a few odd bits of wooden furniture that Jan had fashioned himself. We mused over the possible stories behind these objects, and they began to inspire our own work. Leslie made drawings and photos of the things around the house, while Chris and I thought about Jan when we wrote. We imagined his spirit as a benevolent companion to our efforts as poor artists under the tiny, anonymous roofs of Paris. We imagined that somehow he was rooting for us, that he would have related to our plight.

The three of us were living on just a few bucks a day, which was enough to split up a 500-gram bag of pasta or rice, and add in some cheap protein, like a can of tuna, leaving enough left over for the obligatory bottle of rotgut wine. Maybe we'd splurge on some tomato sauce, or butter, if one of us had scored some extra change that day. But we didn't earn too much, since none of us left home very often. We were mostly focused on our creative endeavors. Not to mention that we were in the Montmartre neighborhood, at the far north end of town, so any time one of us wanted to visit our friends, or our old haunts in the downtown scene, it involved more than an hour of walking each way. We certainly faced some challenges that year, but thanks to Mark, Anthony, and Chris, at least none of us were on the street. We weren't starving to death. We all had someplace to work on our art. And for the time being, none of us (except Jan) were dead. We tried our best to honor Jan's memory, and to see ourselves as kings rather than dogs.

We carried on living there this way for a few months, without any word from Jan's family, but one day, when Leslie and I were out of town on a little hitchhiking trip, Chris was surprised by the arrival of Jan's father at the door. The father was equally surprised, not knowing who Chris was, and expecting either to find the place empty or maybe to run into Anthony. According to the father's side of the story, Anthony had simply stopped sending him the rent, some months prior, with no explanation. So he had flown in from Germany to square things away with Jan's apartment and put it up for sale. He told Chris that he knew Anthony was in town, and had spoken to him by phone, but that Anthony had been dodging him. Chris tried to be diplomatic and did his best to work out what was going on. He got in touch with Anthony himself, but Anthony was evasive about his reasons for avoiding the father. So Chris wound up dealing with the entire situation on his own.

Jan's father was confused about Anthony's disappearing act, and also about the story that led up to his son's apartment being full of people he didn't know who weren't paying him any rent. Chris could easily have just split, and let the chips of the situation fall where they may, but instead he hung in there, out of sheer sympathy and class, and looked for a solution that would appease everyone involved. He didn't want Jan's grieving father to be left holding the bag during an already tragic time for his family, and he didn't want Leslie and me to return home only to find that we were back on the streets. Jan's father had his understandable doubts about leaving the apartment in the care of three people he didn't know, so Chris took the entirety of his savings and gave it to him in good faith, as a couple months' advance rent, so that we could stay on while he was making his preparations to sell the place. Jan's father was touched by this gesture, and I think he was happy to know that the place his son had left behind was of sincere use to some creative young people. He graciously allowed us to stay there until he found a buyer, and he only took a few of Jan's furniture items with him before telling us that we could help ourselves to anything there that we might need.

When the time came for the new owner to move in, it was Chris who found the lead on our next home: a tiny little top-floor, slant-roofed room in one of the old buildings on the Île St-Louis in the middle of the Seine. The night that we moved there, we walked the whole way across town, carrying with us a pile of the essentials we'd adopted at Jan's place: the little cutting board, the knife with the broken tip, the slotted wooden stirring spoon, as well as the cassette tapes and the chessboard. These things all followed us to that next little room we lived in, and then to the next one after that. Chris kept the place on the island for a while, but Leslie and I eventually moved on to another *chambre de bonne*, back over in Hemingway's old neighborhood off the Left Bank, where we still live today. And still, every night when I cook, I use those kitchen utensils and think briefly of Jan. I try to remember, with every meal I eat, that we live on a fringe, a precipice, a cliff, where sometimes there is only space for us because someone else doesn't get that little bit of luck and decides that it's easier just to leap. To anyone who's living like a dog in Paris tonight, I hope you catch a break. ❧

Isn't That Nice

Halley Parry

Marielle had a tooth yanked from her gum on a Tuesday while most people she knew were gliding around carpeted office buildings moving papers from one window to the other and eating salads from round plastic bowls, their feet secretly bare beneath their desks. After the procedure as she approached her apartment, she remembered that her husband, Simon, would not be at home waiting to tend to her. This was not because Simon would be on call sitting next to his ambulance or tending to other injured people, but because he wasn't her husband anymore.

The rotten, extracted tooth rattled around a plastic orange container shaped like a treasure chest. It was not her tooth to bite with, gnaw with anymore despite its long, troubled history in her mouth. A stray cat switched its tail on a small patch of dirt next to the steps leading to the door of her building. Her apartment sat three stories directly above a dress shop, the kind of store that only contains seven or eight items, as if each dress would become violent if left too near a competitor. The beta fish of dresses. She preferred crowded shops where you can't distinguish one item from another until you pull it out, and leave empty handed because nothing looks quite as beautiful when held up by itself but merely compliments its rack mates. She examined the gaping hole in the front of her mouth in the reflection of the window, actively disregarding the eyebrow raise from the woman behind the counter.

For several weeks after preschool let out for the summer, a neighbor's daughter was dispatched to Marielle's house for containment and snacks while the girl's mother, a robust woman named Ophelie, conducted research about the details of her own infanthood. Specifically, who her birth mother might be. Little Hattie was parked in a wooden chair with the excess of a long tablecloth pulled across her head when Marielle came in. Her stuffed bear Frizzy was on the floor smiling his yarn smile. "She was *just here*," Marielle mused falsely with a smile, fewer teeth, "I guess all of this pie is for me then."

"I'm right HERE!" Hattie squealed, dramatically revealing herself and clearing the table with a comic clatter, a clatter that lasts much longer than the inciting incident and continues smashing gleefully long after it should have ceased. Marielle was still sweeping up broken glass and collecting grains of sugar when Hattie's mother leaned on the buzzer downstairs. Marielle had always hated how a sound could infiltrate the space without her approval. The buzzer rang again, longer. Hattie had salt on her face from tears and was picking blueberries out of the pie, holding her legs very still while Marielle reached under the table for a particularly jagged fragment of vase. The vase had been a gift from Marielle's husband, Simon. His sudden departure from her life made her suspect he was apt to return just as suddenly, so she left the wounded door to her apartment gaping, exposing the warm innards of her apartment to the hallway. She already couldn't remember much about his physical presence. When his name was uttered or floated behind her eyes she thought of a small bump on the back of his head that flaked like a delicate pastry and the night he had crawled into bed making every effort not to touch her by crossing his arms over his chest, sheathed in his favorite sweater and clammy-handed. This was the night after the doctor told her that she was broken, that she could not carry a child in her belly. She pictured rust swirling through her bloodstream, her womb an old safe floating to the bottom of the sea. But she didn't blame the man; the switch of his biology had simply been flipped to *off*.

Hattie was examining the pictures of a children's book with an element of horror in it, a mysterious beast with a hard metal spike for a tail and big round eyes. The beast was unpredictable, and according to her mother, nothing to worry about. "FAERIES" she screamed as if it was an obvious answer to the question no one was able to ask aloud, forgetting momentarily about the mess she had just made: "The beast hates FAERIES because they are beautiful and can fly and live forever until we all EXPLODE." A piece of blueberry launched from her mouth with the force of her XPL. She must know something about science.

Hattie was explaining the beast in more detail than was reflected on the pages of the book when her mother came in through the open door and immediately asked her to please stop, she was not supposed to mention the beast after dark. *Because that's when he is here, I suspect*, said Hattie's eyes. Ophelie whisked herself over to her daughter and ruffled her short blonde hair. She wore a pink faux fur coat that was stained and matted and resembled asbestos torn from the walls of a remodeled home. She wrapped her cold fingers around Marielle's wrists and over her flannel shirt to drag her into the kitchen where she opened a bottle of wine without asking, "I found her," she said, quietly pausing to make a snide comment about Marielle's missing tooth, "I fucking found her." Ophelie had been adopted by a couple in Manhattan when she was two years old. Now, she was spending afternoons at the adoption agency sifting through records after being diagnosed with a rare genetic, if nonfatal, disease. The agency informed her that they could not give her any information about where she came from because she had been turned in by a woman who found her, *"found me,"* she repeated with bug eyes, "outside the supermarket." Marielle did not have time to formulate an appropriate question before Ophelie began to speak again.

"But then we, me and the hag from the agency, found the cops who were there that night when I was dumped. It was on the exact border and the same exact day that they found that tribe of feral people on the mountain."

Marielle remembered the history lesson about the feral tribe, their hairy faces, the headlines and the lawsuits, the updated science textbooks. The skepticism surrounding their DNA tests, when scientists realized these people had more genetic material in common with fossils of early humans than humans today. No one knew how they had remained unseen for so long. And she also remembered that they were suspected to have produced offspring in jail. She remembered how they spat accusatory fingers of drool at camera crews and were all later arrested for one thing or another. One woman, she remembered slowly, had been arrested for eating a live tabby cat. It was missing, its face printed on cheap paper and stapled to every telephone pole on the block. The woman was using a staple to clean her teeth when they found her—she'd stabbed the officer with the staple, leaving a tiny puncture wound on his thumb that bled for days.

Ophelie sat down, "So what they think is, I am the direct descendent of a yeti. Half yeti, maybe. At least this explains my Pangaea forehead and inability to keep my arms properly shaved." She was taking this news surprisingly well. Marielle wasn't even sure how to classify this news. Ophelie had a set of adoring parents and a latent desire for fame, but surprises had never settled well with her. Hattie's genesis had unwound her and stitched her back together in a particular chaotic shape and this revelation had the potential to nibble at the stitches with a set of pointy teeth.

"The beast is here," said Hattie from the doorway to the kitchen, flat-footed and flat voiced. She was having an intense conversation in glances with the space just behind Marielle, who couldn't help it and turned around slowly to see what was behind her. There was, of course, nothing there. "He's hungry," said Hattie and placed some pie on the ground.

Hattie's beast lives on a tall island in the middle of the sea on a planet pasted with clouds. These are her words. Paste is how a child makes things stay where they could not otherwise. It is impossible to tell how large or small the beast is; it could be as small as a tealeaf or as large as a lumbering mammoth. No one knows how large the planet is, either. The sea that the island juts from is the color of strong black tea and glints from the scales of thousands of tiny silver sea creatures that dance in roils and fall like bubbles in a boiling pot. She complicates the picture book with her own drawings, self-portraits, rudely inserting herself into the narrative as she had inserted herself into the narrative of her mother's body.

"You aren't afraid of the beast anymore?" said Ophelie in disbelief.

"He can't come unstuck yet from the book." At this, Hattie was ushered out of the room and into her own apartment down the street.

A square of light from an adjacent window fell onto the bed over the lump of Marielle's body in the otherwise dark room. As she lay perfectly still under a mound of blankets in an attempt to warm one area of the bed as efficiently as possible, a muffled alarm began to scream beneath her. It began as a low tone and escalated quickly. She tried to ignore its shrill whine but it coaxed her into wakefulness and she climbed, shivering, from bed and fastened a robe around her waist. The alarm was muffled by the floorboards she placed her feet on and lifted them from, one after the other until she reached her front door, which she left ajar even in sleep. She looked out her kitchen window onto the street, empty save for several parked cars. There was no chaos. The only chaos existed in her head where sound stopped being waves and turned to noise. A light was flashing intermittently below her, illuminating the sidewalk that was damp from an earlier rain. The whole scene appeared to be made of glass.

She retrieved her phone from the bedside table and dialed 9-1-1. The dispatcher answered, "What's the address? Did you see an intruder? If you didn't see an intruder or any evidence of a crime, I can't send someone down there. We have pressing emergencies that . . . can you hold?" She held. She peeled a banana and began to eat it. The aroma filled the kitchen. Then the banana started to taste metallic, like she was cutting it with razor blades instead of her teeth. The banana came away from her mouth red. The alarm escalated again, grew louder and more insistent. It made her veins pulse, the taste in her mouth became stronger and she spit on the floor, red, like she'd just flossed her teeth with rusty wire. She took another pill and stuffed her mouth with the cotton swabs they had sent her home with in a small plastic bag. The cotton tasted like fresh laundry and when the emergency dispatcher came back on the line, she tried to speak but the sound wouldn't escape through the cloth, it muffled her words. She wrapped the blanket strewn on the back of the couch around her ears and was lulled to sleep on the couch by steady, unanswered cries for help.

The next morning, in silence, she took two more pills and called in sick from work. She awoke in a daze hours later to Hattie humming softly on the floor beside her. Hattie's voice was low, a cheerful little growl, "You napped," she said, "I came in myself. I'm hungry." Marielle's stomach bowed towards her spine, hungry too, and when she stood up the world flashed bright. She boiled water for spaghetti and sliced an avocado in half, throwing the knife into the pit to lift it from its flesh, while Hattie floated on imaginary wings around the kitchen table. She drained the noodles and filled each half of avocado with mini shrimp from the freezer, they would thaw before it was time to eat. The pit of the avocado landed with a dull thud on top of trash in the bin. The curve of the shrimp bodies would heat to room temperature, be consumed, and then heat for life in their human bellies before being expelled.

Hattie began eating the shrimp frozen because she liked strawberry popsicles. It was cold but sunny so they went out to eat on the stoop. Hattie placed her small white plate one step above where she sat and Marielle placed hers one step below, next to her feet. She leaned around the banister and peered into the shop window. The woman behind the counter was looking at her fingernail as though on the brink of a great, but puzzling, discovery. She was sweating, Marielle could tell because she wiped her forehead with a small white square of cloth, too small to be a handkerchief. It reminded Marielle of the gauze and the pasta in her mouth began to taste like a sweater Simon used to wear under his uniform when it was cold. She had once tried to take the sweater off with her teeth but it took much too long, and she found he was wearing another sweater underneath. It was impossible to undress him.

The entire storefront was a window that had been perfectly polished until it appeared invisible. One short white dress hung on a metal mannequin in the center of the store. Its shoulders were structured like two paper airplanes and the shopgirls' part was as straight as a runway down the center of her head. She moved from behind the small counter and adjusted a sleeve of the dress on display, making no discernable difference, but the adjustment appeared to satisfy her. She resumed her post in the sterile greenhouse, a light wind moving among the leaves. Marielle pushed on the gum where her tooth used to be and it throbbed. Several minutes later, Ophelie turned the corner and approached the stoop, a manila folder under her arm bursting with crisp white paper. Marielle knew it had something to do with the woman, her mother, but didn't ask. Ophelie swept Hattie from the porch and down the street, she placed a warm hand on Marielle's knee and Hattie mimicked the gesture on her foot in a gesture of goodbye.

Marielle descended the stairs behind them, leaving the dishes where they sat, and entered the shop to see if perhaps the alarm from the night before had come from inside. She caught a glimpse of herself in a mirror to the left of the entrance, her jeans fit poorly and her t-shirt was wrinkled and yellowing in the armpits. The girl behind the counter raised her eyes but did not utter a word of greeting as Marielle approached the counter. She placed both hands on the cold surface and the girl still did not raise her head. She was thin, her collarbones stuck out through her white silk top which seemed to not be touching any part of her body but hovering around her. Marielle suddenly remembered her tooth, and that speaking would reveal its absence. This was not an environment for missing teeth. She would be frowned upon. Instead, she smiled with closed lips and in order to explain her charge of the counter, she selected a lacy black thong from a bowl and purchased it in silence, how sophisticated of her. When she emerged back out onto the street she pushed onto her gum harder with a dirty finger and looked down to realize that the thong was an XS,

PETITE and had cost her forty-six dollars she didn't have. The stray cat ate the leftover shrimp on the stoop.

Hattie let herself in promptly after school the next day and sat quietly until the sun set. Marielle woke up on the couch and found her in the kitchen on tiptoe, slicing a banana with the handle of a serving spoon. When Ophelie swept through the door, Hattie was elaborating on her day with a mouthful of banana, ". . . and his teacups are made of dust. No, his teacups are made of sticks and his tea is dust which is why he always has a cough," she coughed to elaborate before continuing, "and all over the mountain are yellow flowers that grow pomegranate seeds and that's what he eats."

Ophelie's teeth were stained with red. She announced that she was done with research, she had no more interest in learning about her mother and Hattie would no longer need to spend afternoons with Marielle. Her eyes wouldn't focus and Hattie looked at Marielle as though she knew this mood, her mother should not be questioned or prodded, and Hattie followed her somberly. Marielle was surprised to feel a great sense of loss that Hattie wouldn't be arriving every day. At first, it had seemed like a great burden but she had come to enjoy Hattie's small presence.

Marielle fell asleep before taking any medication, her gum suffered a dull warm pain she had become accustomed to and almost welcomed. The lack of pain in the rest of her body made her feel perfect. She was naked, she hadn't changed the sheets since he left and they were soaked with oils from her skin. As if on cue, the wail of the alarm woke her from a deep sleep and this time she shot from bed immediately. She had dreamt of her wedding, slipping in and out of her dress under observation in rewind and then forward slowly. The petite thong rested, rolled up in a tiny coil, on the kitchen counter.

This time, she zipped up the jeans on the floor next to her bed and went downstairs onto the street. She called 9-1-1 from her cell phone, a different voice from the previous night answered, "What is your emergency."

"Something set off the alarm in the shop below my apartment and it isn't shutting off," she said unsure if the wail had drowned her out entirely. The alarm began to hold its notes longer like a melancholy performer.

"Is there evidence of a break-in or other criminal activity?" the dispatcher took a sip of something next to the mouthpiece.

"No it just keeps going off, the same thing happened last night and no one comes to turn it off."

"Ma'am, unless there is suspicious activity I can't send a car down there."

"What if I told you it was me, I'm breaking into the store."

"Are you, ma'am?"

"No."

"Good night then miss." The liquid he had sipped made him cough before he hung up.

She pressed her nose to the window, leaving a smudge. The interior of the store was completely still, a diorama, the white dress stood in darkness. At intervals in time to the beat of the alarm it was bathed in red light. The color weaponized its purity, blood spilled on a snow-covered garden. She didn't sleep or even close her eyes until the sun rose and the alarm was silenced presumably by its own code, by the finger of the unreadable woman who would remove her coat and place it delicately over a chair behind the counter.

The day passed, and at noon she went to get a new tooth sewn into her gums. It was made specifically for her, and was not noticeably different when she bared her teeth in the small circular mirror. Only she could tell it was an imposter. She missed little Hattie. On her block, a woman was crouching down next to a small boy and pointing at something. Marielle followed her finger which led to the stray cat, curled up behind a dresser that someone had discarded on the curb next to a bag of trash. The woman was enunciating kitty, K-I-T-T-Y and sounded ridiculous, "Isn't that cute? Isn't that nice? He's sleeping!" As Marielle passed she saw, after some scrutiny, that the cat was not sleeping but had starved to death.

As Marielle walked from the kitchen to the living room with a glass of wine later that evening the room erupted into noise with such ferocity that she dropped the glass. It was not the alarm as she initially suspected but her telephone. The glass didn't break, but warm red wine eased onto the carpet like a tide. She answered the phone on the second ring, it was nearly 10 o'clock. It was Hattie and she sounded scared, there was a dish clattering in the background.
"Mama made dinner and it tastes bad," she whispered.
"What do you mean it tastes bad."
"It's not dinner," Hattie's voice rose with panic.
"I'll come over, hang tight."

She walked to the building where Ophelie and Hattie lived alone in the garden apartment. There was a small arrangement of doll furniture on the curb, a bed made from cardboard and matches, a chair that would seat someone just larger than the person who was sized to sleep in the bed, a tattered blanket, a tiny jar of jam that reminded Marielle of continental breakfasts at cheap motels and a small flower pot full of Styrofoam peanuts. She recognized these objects, they were Hattie's toys, placed on the street like old junk.

She pushed tentatively at the buzzer, twice, three times until Ophelie came to the door. She was speaking as if she had started a conversation long before Marielle arrived, "And did you know," she said, frantically slicing a chicken and placing it onto empty plates and picking what appeared to be a feather from between her teeth but couldn't be, "that the women got raped by the hunters that found them, that those were the babies they gave birth to?" Marielle looked closer. The chicken was completely raw, bleeding onto the plates and the table was set for five people.

Before Marielle had a chance to answer, Hattie lowered her head and vomited into a soup bowl on the table in front of her, perfectly refilling it, and cried with her head in her hands. Ophelie laughed a wicked peal that ended in one long note.

Emerging from stun into ferocity, Marielle pointed to Hattie's fork, "Put that down," she said, "Ophelie, go to bed. I'm taking your daughter to my apartment for a sleepover." Ophelie's face softened, as her hand clenched around utensils, "My daughter?" She lunged before falling to the ground with the force of her own sobs. She lay among them. Marielle whispered, "Get yourself together."

"Hattie, why is Frizzy's furniture on the sidewalk?" she stepped to Hattie and took her hand, crouched on her knees.

"He's moving out, he hates it here, and he particliary *hates mama*," she screamed weakly as though she were trying to scream in a nightmare, dry and soft. Frizzy sat propped in the chair next to her, disturbed. Marielle was wrong. This was bad news and Ophelie was taking it murderously.

Marielle led Hattie outside where she promptly vomited on the sidewalk, drenching Frizzy and her own front with bile. She wept and cradled her stomach. Marielle pulled her hair from her forehead which was burning hot and lifted her off the ground, smearing vomit on her sweater but not minding. With her other hand she reached into her pocket for her phone and began dialing 9-1-1, again. The memory of her recent failures with those particular digits stopped her and instead she did something she swore never to do again, she called Simon. He had a fondness for Hattie and would know what to do from a medical perspective at least. Hattie tugged on her hair, wanting to be let down. Marielle placed her on the ground where she bent down and scooped up Frizzy's match bed from the curb, one-eighth his size, and returned to slump against the back of Marielle's legs. Frizzy would need somewhere to sleep. Simon answered on the third ring of the second call, "What."

She lifted Hattie back up and said with the strain of the little body ascending in her voice said, "Hattie's been poisoned by raw chicken and possibly something else I need help. She's really sick."

"Jesus Christ Elle. Please tell me you aren't making this up," he said.

"No, I need you to come help me, it's a sick child." She was silent while he agreed, she apologized for the call and continued the journey down the block where she carried Hattie up the stairs clumsily, Hattie repeatedly head-butting her in the mouth like a tiny goat, and placed her gently on a towel on the bed. She dreaded his arrival but carried within her a deep desire to see him, to remember his face. She went into the front of the apartment and closed the front door. She wished she hadn't apologized. As she turned the lock, the alarm began to scream and a sound mimicked it from the bedroom.

Marielle clamped her jaw with surprise and her new tooth chose this moment to fall from her mouth in a cliff dive to the floor where it crashed with such ferocity that it overpowered the competing wails for just a moment. The pain was acute. She took one pill, two, three, placing her mouth directly under the faucet. The water splashed joyfully on her face and neck. She immediately began to feel the numbing effects of the pills on her body and mind. Hattie was silenced but the alarm carried on with unrelenting vigor, tearing through the fiber of her ears into the intricate network where her thoughts nested. She did not know where Simon was coming from or how long it would take him to arrive, how long had it been since she called? Frizzy stank and she placed him in the sink with the water still running before checking to make sure Hattie was alive, her pulse thrummed under the skin of her neck. She checked her own pulse too, because life is a fragile thing. She embroidered this on a pillow in her mind. She would wash Frizzy until the water ran clean.

A steady wind grazed her face and she felt her eyes opening and closing instinctually to protect themselves. The alarm seemed louder tonight, the shop darker. The dress shone like a moon instead, carrying within it an inherent vital brightness. She picked up a metal chair chained to the café next to the shop and used the leg, which reached just far enough, to shatter the front window of the store. Then she reluctantly dialed 9-1-1.

"There has been a break-in at a shop on 3rd street," she paused, eyeing the dress, "two doors down from my apartment and they've broken a window," she went on, "it's two men, one tall and one short and they are wearing all black and they were both coughing aggressively." She remembered that little details make everything more believable, "actually just one of them was coughing, but so aggressively it sounded like two."

When she hung up, she walked idly through the hole she had created and circled the dress like a predator, the red light of the alarm had begun flashing rapidly, now bathing both her and the dress in its violent hue. She ran her finger over the fabric and licked it, as though she had just touched a delicious cake and tried to hide the evidence. She turned and caught a glimpse of herself in the long mirror made for examining bodies in beautiful things. She was drooling slightly, the pills, she wiped it away and smiled a toothless grin at herself. She remembered something then about the wild women, one in particular. Before she was cleaned up, before she was placed somewhere in the city, they had led this particular wild woman into a room with a mirror and observed her. The first thing she did was throw herself at the mirror. It took her a moment to realize that she was seeing herself for the first time. She placed her hands on the mirror and leaned in, moving them up and down in precise measurements. She found she could not let go of her own reflected hands and wept at her own image. When the image wept back, she laughed. When her reflection laughed, she looked around for an explanation. Her reflection looked around for an explanation, too, but she couldn't see it when she turned her head.

Marielle carefully unzipped the back of the dress and lifted it from the mannequin. It was weightless. She shoved the dress under her sweater and thought of the look the saleswoman would give her. *The delicate structure! You'll wrinkle the fabric! Monster, crazy bitch, the most unsophisticated woman in the world!*

She crunched back over the mound of broken glass as though they were fallen leaves, nearly slicing her cheek on the jagged wall of the window, sprinted into her apartment and threw the dress down on the couch where it reclined delicately to rest. She heard sirens in the distance approaching, the sounds swirling like a physical thing from all directions. She put on a jacket and went back onto the street. She was standing on the sidewalk when the first police car pulled up, blue lights flashing and giving the whole scene an aquarium glow. Before she had a chance to speak, the man in the passenger seat had her hands behind her back and was snapping handcuffs over them. She thought about struggling but was swimming. She knew that this could be cleared up easily with a few simple words but the shock had muted her. The officer got her blood on his hands and checked the wound on her cheek gruffly, certainly filed it as evidence of her guilt. So, she had cut her cheek after all.

Then she recognized a plain car pulling up to the curb. Simon stepped out of the driver's seat and left the headlights on, a diver's spotlight in the swirling blue sea of light. He exchanged some words with the cop, patted him on the shoulder. It appeared to pain him to admit that he was acquainted with the bleeding woman in handcuffs on the sidewalk. He must have known the police officer as well, because he apologized profusely as he uncuffed her and pawed her face strangely. She explained that she had been the one to call the police and reiterated her description of the burglars to a "how unusual, they took one dress," from the officer.

She realized she was speaking with a lisp. Her husband led her upstairs, she didn't limp, "Hattie's in the bedroom." She wouldn't thank him again or apologize. She slurred, he didn't ask her many questions. Simon opened the door with his own key, but found that it was unlocked and shook his head. He helped her gently lay down on the couch, on top of the dress. She could feel the fabric of it on the back of her arms and she smiled. He either did not notice the dress or chose not to, and took his bulky backpack with him into the bedroom.

She heard him ask Hattie what her favorite color was, which was the wrong question. Hattie didn't believe in favorite colors. She knew, already, that one color was meaningless without the others. She had the tenacity of an elderly politician who would never be elected but continues to run every year. Hattie choked on the words she was saying, and they were followed by the sound of vomit in a bowl, and Marielle's husband came into the living room looking for pen and paper, "How does she know the word 'contract'? I don't think she remembers me," he sighed, disrupting the top layer of sugar in the bowl on the kitchen table. Marielle, wide-awake, lay on the couch and listened to the sounds of this man taking care of a child in what was once their bed together. She felt a shallow, tortured emotion, like trying to pick an invisible hair from your tongue and giving up.

A commotion in the kitchen captured her attention. Frizzy was drenched and trying to hide, she saw his leg slip down into the drain and the sound of the water running changed. It was no longer water falling on steel but water falling into more water. His head lowered into the sink but his expression did not change.

Her husband's voice surprised her before she could prevent Frizzy from drowning, "Hattie will be fine, it was just a powerful reaction to the raw meat and stress. I've given her something for infection." He picked up the thong on the counter, "What's this? You've never worn anything like this before." Before he could say, *It doesn't suit you,* he stepped on the tooth that had fallen from her mouth earlier and barked. She wanted him to stay.

"You'll be okay with a full house tonight, then?" he said, moving towards the front door, which was now open.

Not quite a full house, she thought to herself, *there is still one empty bed.* When she was alone she took teeth, both rot and enamel and placed them side by side in Frizzy's bed, covering them gently with a piece of gauze. They were the only occupants of the house small enough to fit. Then she put on the dress and climbed in bed next to Hattie who was sleeping peacefully. The water from the sink rose to the brim of the basin and slowly began to flood the apartment while the beast climbed up the fire escape and into her womb. ❧

THE CONFESSIONS OF NOA WEBER

Lisa A. Phillips

My recommendation: *The Confessions of Noa Weber,* by Gail Hareven. It's part of the unsung literary tradition of narratives of female romantic abjection—unsung because the whole idea, particularly when it comes to female-on-male yearning, is a kind of a feminist nightmare, a secret shame outed. He loves me not, but I love him—stubbornly, painfully, and in a life-defining way. The fish does need the bicycle, and badly.

Early classics of this tradition include several of Sappho's poem fragments and Charlotte Brontë's *Villette,* along with her passionate letters to Constantin Héger, the Belgian school master she was obsessed with. The gloves come off completely in the late 20th century in Chris Kraus's intellectually, erotically, and emotionally excessive *I Love Dick.* And when I say excessive, I don't mean that in a bad way—it's the entire point of this not-quite-memoir/not-quite-novel about the author/narrator's obsession with an academic named Dick. It's excessive because it's an obsession and that's the entire point. It's the food you can't stop eating because it never satisfies, the endless soapbox speech in the town square, the hot swelling between your legs that won't subside.

Hareven's *Confessions* is a much quieter book. It's my recommendation because it's unsentimentally hopeful, an uncommon quality in stories of otherwise doomed unrequited love. In *Confessions,* Noa, an Israeli attorney and author of a series of feminist detective novels, quits her job to write an account of her unrequited love for Alek, a peripatetic Russian immigrant journalist and the father of her daughter. She is hoping for a kind of catharsis of her obsession, which she calls her "dybbuk," the vindictive possessing spirit of Jewish mythology. But right away it's doubtful she'll be able to purge her love for Alek, which she experiences as a "transcendence"—not an easy thing to forsake.

The stubbornness of unrequited love is fundamentally subversive: I want you, and I'm going to keep wanting you, even if you don't want me. That's why female stalker movies like *Fatal Attraction* are both troubling and liberating—these viragos are *fuck you*'s to anyone who's been tossed aside by some selfish prick. Noa is no stalker. In fact she's admittedly passive. At one point in the book she doesn't see Alek for a decade. Yet, she persists not only in loving him, but also in secretly nurturing the self who loves, even as her love contradicts contemporary notions of what's "healthy" in life and relationships.

And what comes of this rebel state? She lives ostensibly for Alek and despite him. At her first legal trial she imagines him there, her arguments made to impress him. Her detective novels make her a pop culture feminist icon, her fictional heroine's independence in stalwart contrast to her own irrational need. She shields her daughter from her obsession. Alek is entwined in her strength and her successes, a kind of lifelong muse. But he's also a constant torment.

I first read *Confessions* as I was starting my own book about unrequited love. My book is nonfiction, blending my own long-ago story of obsession with an exploration of why we succumb to this kind of fix. Several months after *Unrequited* was published, the man I was obsessed with briefly came back into my life. We'd been out of touch for fifteen years. During a good deal of that time, he lived in me as material—he appears in several places in the book—but I can safely say that however consumed I was by writing the book, I was no longer obsessed with *him*. Reconnecting through messages and a single phone call caused, shall we say, a significant relapse. Longing for him again was a surreal experience, given the years and thousands of miles that separated us. I was in a completely different place in my life—married, a mother, firmly entrenched in my career. Nevertheless, I thought, "I will carry this feeling to my grave." And I was ashamed. I was the woman who *wrote the book on romantic obsession*. How could this have been happening to me?

I returned to *Confessions* like a bible, seeking insight into what I was going through. Like Noa, I had done the unrequited-love-as-muse thing, writing myself into a competent life that contrasted with my need. Like Noa, I was a Jew who wanted to be rid of her dybbuk. I pondered her attachment to the "transcendence" her unrequited love allowed—an irony given her resolute refusal to embrace Jewish spirituality as her daughter, a rabbi-in-training, has. Or perhaps this isn't ironic? In Judaism, God must remain not only unseen but also unimaginable. God's name can't be said, God's face can't be depicted. A classic early Hebrew school lesson is to ask children what they imagine God to look like. A common answer in the classroom I was in was a bearded rabbi. Then, the children are told gently that the Jewish God has no form or figure. Christianity, in contrast, sees Christ as a bridge from humans to God, as an evangelical librarian in Iowa once explained to me, drawing a little diagram to underscore his point. Perhaps Christianity isn't really the less sensual religion, as contemporary Jews tend to believe. It acknowledges the human desire for form and flesh in both physical and spiritual longings.

I began to think of Noa's desire as not so much a contradiction to her public persona but its necessary shadow. As she describes it, her love for Alek is the "only thing that gives me a sense of space." We are, in our culture, terrible at giving ourselves a sense of space—aimless, troubling, seemingly unproductive space in which we live with our deepest spiritual, emotional, and creative questions. It's very hard to find a space where we can take off the masks we wear each day, masks that for women can be particularly oppressive. There's the work mask, the wife mask, the caretaker mask, the mother mask. The mask of femininity, constantly re-evaluated with age: What to hide? What to reveal? What to color, to depilate?

I was also struggling with the author mask, so very different from the unmasked feeling of actually writing *Unrequited*. The author mask often required me to distill my book into talking points and, worse, "tips" for magazines and web sites—often about "how to get over him for good." For me, the more complex and important aspect of my book was more in line with Noa's experience of obsession. Sometimes, living with an unrequited love is the point, not getting over it. That withholding beloved is the bridge to an amorphous, messy state of being, a place where you aren't following all the rules and you aren't wearing a mask, a place that can be expansive and transformative. Therein lay another irony: Being the author of *Unrequited,* a book that is as confessional as it is informative, was pushing me to wear the mask of togetherness, of being an "expert," of saying it's all settled, I'm over it, and you can be, too! Fiction, and writers of fiction, are generally free of such pressures, though I understand Edith Wharton got some major heck for not getting Lawrence and Lily together at the end of *The House of Mirth.*

The Confessions of Noa Weber is a book about a woman unmasked. I don't think this is very common, in fiction and in life. I don't believe that unrequited love is the only way we can find space and take off our masks. And, dutiful author/expert that I am, I'm obliged to say that being romantically obsessed doesn't guarantee transcendence—it's a volatile state and can simply be too ruinous to be enlightening. But some of us may, at certain junctures, need the form of an enigmatic and withholding beloved—not a Christ, definitely, but not exactly an anti-Christ either—to push us to experience the self behind the masks. And no matter how all-consuming the beloved other seems, the self is ultimately what unrequited love is about. *Confessions* helps me remember that when unrequited love thrusts itself into my life, I can see it as a push, however painful, toward a more authentic existence. I don't want to give a spoiler about how Noa's story ends. But let's just say that I don't believe that either of us will be taking our phantom lovers to our graves.   ❧

The Size of It

Andrea Cohen

They made oceans
big so one boat

going would seem
small. The sail

of your dinghy
obliterates the sun:

they were wrong.

Jehova

Andrea Cohen

If you've seen
the light you've

seen how
bright it is,

and dressed in
Sunday's best

intent, how
could you not

climb toward
the darkest

door and not
stop knocking?

Rabbit Hole

Andrea Cohen

Never move, my swell
friend Alice says, and

you'll never feel pain.
But never moving

bruises too—everything
with never stings.

Bootstraps

Andrea Cohen

So you pulled
them up. What

cobbler made
those shoes

and whose
hands, asking

nothing, gave
them to you?

Pebble

Andrea Cohen

I placed a pebble
where you were—

so you'd know
where to come

back to and how
hard days are.

Chair

Andrea Cohen

Not there—
the easy
chair recalls
all of you
too easily.
Sit instead
in the folding
chair, the one
that forgets every-
thing—save
collapsing
when
you
vanish.

Invitation

Lia Purpura

Come close
is only one way,
my way,
entirely my terms
and requiring belief
in a goodness
I imagine
is not a bird's thought
about ease and the world
a safe place
best expressed by
wariness and
me at a distance.

Eft

Jeffrey Harrison

Tiny flicker
hiding
in wet leaves,
infant flame
cool to my
monstrous fingers,
you look at me
inscrutably
with your
minute eye,
your mouth
a straight line,
neither smile
nor frown.

Little wriggler,
orange spy,
you seem to be
keeping a secret.
Even your name,
which means
nothing to you,
feels cryptic,
incomplete,
part of a word—
the way you slip
into the cleft
between rocks
when I let you go.

February Morning

Jeffrey Harrison

Sunday morning, I hear the dog
whining upstairs—but the dog
hasn't been upstairs in years,

and a glance confirms he's
right here at my feet, dozing
under the kitchen table.

Which means my wife is crying.
I hold my breath a second,
listen. What could be wrong?

What sadness is it
she's held inside that now
comes out in tears?

"Are you okay?" I call up.
"Yes," she calls back down,
sounding perfectly cheerful—

she's wiping the condensation
from our bedroom windows
and will be right down.

I listen to the squeaking
of paper towel against wet glass,
now recognizable,

though it's too late
for me to wipe away
the residue of sadness.

Newly Met

April Ossmann

If I told you
I saw your soul,
would you judge me
inappropriate,
too intimate
for comfort—
or disbelieve me?
If you asked
for a description,
would I admit
you glowed, golden
as these late
northern afternoons,
whose slanted autumn light
makes green fire
of a backlit tree's
shimmering leaves,
and balances
me perfectly,
on the tightrope
between yearning
and content,
as if I finally understood
what beauty meant
to tell me?

Camel In The Room

Tara Skurtu

On the train to Brașov I'm reading
student poems. Over and over I write:
be a video camera. I think movie
scenes. The man who invented
a thing everyone wants throws
himself through a boardroom
window. An old man hammers
his old friend's head into
his breakfast plate. A forest:
two lovers, forbidden to love,
unable not to, develop a code,
and behind them a camel—
once a person unable to fall
in love and condemned to choose
a mateless animal whose body
he'd inhabit, roam eternity next
to this couple gesturing desires
behind their backs—enters.
Over shitty beer and wine
you tell me you rode a camel
in Morocco last week, wanted
to make it to Casablanca.
You point to your chest and say
feel, tap your head and say *can't*.
Intimacy is the camel in this room,
and you walk in and out of it,
espresso and cigarette in one hand.
Take this water bottle, you say.
Say you need to fill it with water
from home. You're pointing
to your chest and shaking
a nearly empty bottle in my face.
The young couple against the window
hasn't stopped kissing for over an hour.

Say you need this specific water
to survive. I watch the camel become
you become the elephant become
the room. Sometimes it's the room
and not the elephant, so today
I'll substitute one room for another.
I'll go from this compartment
to the classroom to the bistro
to the bath. I'm going to fill
my deep tub with a whole box
of salts, close my eyes,
pretend I'm in an ocean
of my own making.

Port of Miami, from the MacArthur Causeway

Ricardo Pau-Llosa

It is the sea that is misplaced—
nervous bulk a cupped palm
can sweep into a glitter of dust.
On it the heaviest angles of rust
rise, laden. The hidden helm
lurks its screens and satellites

past rigging and chain, the ancient
mask of a familiar mystery.
Buoyancy is number's boring miracle,
the fruit of tangled sums and symbols
Greek with decimals. Would infinity
be as uncapped, we'd put a dent

in useless chatter about divine
conditions. The barge passes liners
loading cities of fat tourists
with boarding drinks in hand. The dizziest
outshout the tugging machinery
that likewise baffles the eye's supine

reasoning. In the Cave, even light
is shadow that mauls as it apes its origins.
Laws we must dive for. All else is ripple
and spray. A tipsy Cleopatra, visible
from here, points in spills to the towering
barge fading out of sight.

Return to Atomic City

Nancy Dickeman

One day I return, standing
at the house where my father hunched
over the periodic table and my mother scrubbed
the sandstorm's grit
from my face.

The tour bus drives through Hanford's acres, past
the cocooned cores, past the B Reactor
in whose tall rooms plutonium was rushed
for the second bomb, falling
so quickly on the heels
of the first dead.

The bus heaves
past the sacred rolling mounds
the tribes call Mooli Mooli,
pausing at the subterranean
storage tanks. Here radioactive waste crosses
the boundaries of its metal shells,
slipping into the earth.

Nightfall, and the moon flares
like a spindle of fire on the river.
I plunge my hands beneath the surface
but nothing washes off,
the hot particulates long ago
burrowed into me.

Handyman Imagines The Battle Of Pueblo

Juan Morales

When everyone has turned to biting
each other, to emptying
every grocery store in town,
and to sieging out the end times,
we don't know why we didn't leave for the mountains
in our eyeshot.

Our feet got dirty enough in vacant lots
and beat up streets with
road cones coaxing us
how to leave this rest stop town.
The heat challenged our souls to keep it together,

hopeful for afternoon rains to nourish
gardens hidden in
Bessemer backyards. We used to feast
at east-side taquerias on one-way streets.
We used to bike through the avenues to wander

downtown, through alleys
graffiti fresh, finding our way
to where the river paralleled limestone barrens,
and levee murals
for local gods that once stretched into sunset.

We want the mill to spew yawns all night,
coal trains to whistle, crashes of train cars
loading again,
so we fortify and clear out
the dead ones,
to make this town home again.

Self Portrait Of Handyman Sanding Floors

Juan Morales

I disappear under respirator and goggles.
I'm a survivor in a wasteland
separated into dining room, living room,
bedroom one, and bedroom two.
Under my mask, I taste the dust
and blink it out of my eyes.
The sander is a few decades old and weighs
more than I do. It rumbles the floors
then glides, the spinning wheels chewing off the stains,
scratches, and gouges
saved over the last two generations
in the floor that will be swept and wiped
into the soft honey touch
of an aftermath that lies beneath.

from The Pocket Oracle

Sharon Dolin

Always have something in reserve
            —after Baltasar Gracián

Leave some spirit
in the flagon » flanken

on the spear » have chocolate
pastilles in a jar »

a jar of eels » the past
is chalk » hawk something

absurd or overheard:

ancient   artifact   unearthed
new shards of Sappho's verse

from the tohubohu
a new universe.

Iphigenia, Ascending

Bailey Spencer

Go ahead:
bring a knife to my neck
that the winds might turn.
How I long for the altar,
the clean gleam of blade.
I was born strong
but now I am not. My limbs
are twisted roots: anemic
carrots, jaundiced beets.
Aching cervine spine.
Boil until the difference
between animal and vegetable
has cooked off. All things
eventually weaken, go soft
and bendable. Skin parts,
slopes slowly into a wound.
This is the body that will
launch showering arrows,
upset the grave-still seas.

Clench

Michele Glazer

His toes clenched. All of him
Went into the fire. Conjure
His body empty—that sack—that final
Ruin I can't separate my father
From his body,　burn it or bury
It they said you have to
　　　　　　　make a choice.　More dark
Than I thought possible, more topo-
Graphical than thought if thought
Could be almost
Riverbed. From every direction
You are one
Long night poured into another night.
While your feet
Were still recognizable as feet I
Wanted to place
The bottoms of my own against them.

Peony

Michele Glazer

She. Cutting white peonies to place near his head.
She. Insisting he leave

with something sweet (the world
as water turning to stone

to be that lost
in the place he lived).

In a cave like this,
the folded hard shapes and the groaning.

The man who wouldn't eat couldn't die.
The man who couldn't die is almost pure

sound, Vivaldi
playing all the time, she thinks

to keep the mind
off his body.

She sits in some front row

crosses a leg. Adjusts a bum. Thinks of him.
Thinks music cannot be made

larger than pain.
His fine mind

a fistful of moths,
and his eyes

and they are cousin and weary, and yellow and true.

Late Summer

Gail Mazur

I stood on the flats with the sandpipers and the gulls. The flock of pipers was not afraid of the enormous fierce-looking gulls, and the gulls were unafraid of me.

And none of us was diminished by the other.

The harsh cries of those gulls, the piping syllabics of such tiny running birds, the invisible protein they foraged.

Their meticulous little bills, their genius at finding in the biofilm what they needed.

Soon all but the gulls would leave, their season here over, and I, too, would leave.

When I walked back to the shore over tide-strewn pebbles and the jagged shells of oysters and scallops and crabs, my feet had become a child's feet again, uncomplaining, pliant.

Time had gone by, but in those moments, there was no pain. I recalled nothing of grief or fear or despair.

Grief, fear, despair—as if I were sleepwalking, those were not the elements of that August afternoon.

How To Avoid A Crash

Major Jackson

Some mornings riding to work
on a road bike up a busy thoroughfare,
my hands tight around the handlebars,
I think of my face buried in the clavicles
of the women I barely knew, eyes clenched,
dispensing a slaughterhouse of whispers
in low-lit rooms of some newly-built hotel,
darkened even more by our affair
far away from my wife and their husbands,
like the one who called years after I forgot
his wife's name to say he knew what I did.

Near the off-ramp, a semi-truck's tires squeal
hard up ahead and exhaust fumes nearly blind
as I navigate periodic surges and tons of metal
accelerating by like oversized munitions.

They held tight, like me, full of an emptiness
we so longed to supplant with desire, our muscles
rough pedaling towards an imaginary terminus.

Now I make eye contact, as experts suggest,
with others whose loud music from open windows
or make-up appliqués have no chance
of sending them swerving in my direction,
jarring me off a path I work to keep,
catapulting me, eyes full of terror, over a median
and down the road's unforgiving blacktop.

Tell the Children

Rebecca McGill

In the six years she'd spent as a substitute teacher, she'd known them simply as *the* students. Now, as a full-time lead teacher, she knew them as *her* students. She worried about the use of this possessive. She worried that it would play tricks on her mind. She worried that she'd forget they belonged elsewhere. She worried that when the parents departed from the classroom each morning and the tiny bodies were transformed from *their children* into *her students*, she'd forget that the children had lives beyond the plastic chairs, beyond the posters of innocuous wildlife (baby seals, parrots, cheetahs), beyond the wooden letters that, when connected by magnets, formed an alphabetical train. So she asked them for reminders, notices, tiny postcards from their other lives.

"Draw a picture of your family," she told the students at the Coloring Table—six of them, the particularly capricious, imaginative ones who always avoided the Numbers Booth—and placed sheets of orange construction paper in front of each small body.

Dale, the one who persistently sought a demonstration, asked her how to draw a hammock and pushed towards her the coffee can containing the crayons. Coffee cans acted as her classroom's Tupperware, their aluminum walls encircling the components of her kindergarten classroom: crickets, erasers, pennies, yarn, scraps of paper on which she'd made the students write their career goals because she believed dreams were best born early. In the two weeks since school had begun, her students had quickly identified the importance of the coffee cans; they'd begun bringing in cans from their own kitchens, hoping their cans would later be called to duty to give a home to paper clips, miniature milk trucks, or the class fish, Archer Fleece, who stayed in a can when his tank needed cleaning.

She knelt down beside Dale, removed a black crayon from the can, and drew what looked like a sunbathing C, stretched out and satiated. "See?" she said. "Hammocks are easy."

"No," said Dale. "Not it."

This, above all else, unnerved her about the children: their insistence. They'd come to recognize the power of their eyes; they could identify the world, name and un-name it, accept it and reject it. So, too, did they have the power to deliver this world to others, and they delivered it to her on a daily basis. She nodded her head upon receiving their deliveries because, until this year, she had been a substitute teacher and knew what it meant to distribute faulty restatements of the facts. She'd once told a third-grade classroom that Johnny Appleseed was from Des Moines. So she listened and smiled when Ralph told her that popsicles were made in washing machines, when Anna told her that she had an uncle with wings, and when Glenna said dancing put little black marks on a person's soul.

"Well, what does your hammock look like?" she asked Dale.

He shrugged. "Not that."

She tapped her fingertip against his paper. "Then show me what it looks like," she said and watched as Dale proceeded to draw an object that looked like a spider wearing a cash register on its back.

"Great," she said. "*Terrific.*"

She had never liked squatting down beside the children, and now her knees hurt. They looked silly in front of her, her calves and feet invisible, as though she could represent only part of a person.

Anna looked up from her own drawing and brought her eyes to Dale's creation. "Yes," she said. "Aunt Sally has a hammock, and it does look like that!"

This unnerved her, too: the students used possessives like oxygen when it came to objects, but *my* left their vocabulary when conversation turned towards people, so Aunt Sally belonged to everyone.

"Draw yours, Ms. Til," Dale said, setting down his crayon. He pushed a piece of paper in her direction, driving it towards her with the tips of his fingers.

"Mine?" she asked. "I don't have a hammock."

"Not your hammock," he said. "Your *family.*"

She'd reddened. Of course she'd reddened, her face taking on the color of ground meat, the kind distributed on plates of Styrofoam at the deli. She hated herself for this, what she'd come to call her Meat Face, but the color claimed her cheeks and ears because in the first two weeks of school, the students hadn't asked about her life and now their preconceived notions were coming to call, saying, *A teacher must have a family* and she felt indefensible against their musts.

"Draw your babies! Babies to *kiss,*" said Glenna, drawing her lips together in a pucker. This was another thing about the children: they loved babies. Even the meanest, most off-putting children spoke often—and fondly—of infants they'd seen on the street or read about in the books they carted into the classroom from the library at the end of the hall.

She held the crayon in her hand and watched as the children stopped working on their drawings, putting their own worlds on pause to glimpse at hers. Ralph placed his green crayon behind his ears and crossed his arms over his chest. He enjoyed these postures, the adult signals of judgment and apathy. Once, he'd pinched the bridge of his nose between his fingers and closed his eyes, saying, "You're just not *following* me."

She looked down at the paper, its blank surface asking that she locate her loved ones and collect them on the page, as though cutting and pasting it into 8 1/2" x 11" spaces was what one did with family. She pressed the crayon onto the page and began to draw a stick figure, waxy black against the orange background. On the figure, she drew a large hat, and in its right hand, a shovel.

"Is that you?" Ralph asked.

She nodded.

"You look boring," said Anna, Anna with the knack for identifying the interesting, Anna with an interest in being interesting. She openly discussed her hatred of the color pink, and as her career goal, had chosen *I will sing songs to firemen.*

The shovel had been a last-ditch effort to make her figure look purposeful and mask the empty space above her left and right shoulders. She'd worked towards avoiding this space—in her drawing, in her mind, in her life—but she saw now that the space was as obvious as a thumbprint, rude as profanity, an absence that cultivated the presence of sorrow.

But what else? What else could she draw? Her mental image of her father consisted only of what he must have looked like in his final moments, and the children wouldn't want to see it, the smack of the deer against the windshield, the end of a man with three children under the age of five. And her mother? Too tall, too lanky, too much liquor in hand, too difficult to locate in the backwoods of New Hampshire, too often with a woman who was perhaps her lover or perhaps the only person who demanded nothing. And her twin brothers? One in China—finance, trade, briefcases, hotels that made you sleep in drawers instead of beds— and one in a New York town called Batavia. He never called, except on her birthday, when he inevitably told her she was too *in her own head* and maybe it was time to take the next plane out of there. Now, he'd said. *Now.*

But it seemed better to claim one of her brothers on the page than to claim nothing at all, so she drew a head, arms, legs, hand. Even when the figure was complete, it still looked insufficient and vague.

"Who's that?" asked Anna. "Your husband?"

She blinked at Anna, then looked down at the figure. This was the finishing touch it had needed. At the mere mention of this word—*husband*—the figure acquired new meaning and gave weight to the female figure beside it. So, too, did it give weight to this otherwise flimsy, transparent, laughable approximation of her life.

"Yes," she replied. "That's my husband." This felt less like a lie, and more like a Halloween costume on her tongue.

"What *is* he?" asked Glenna.

The six children—Glenna, Dale, Anna, Ralph, Patrick, and Isabelle—pitched their bodies forward, clamoring to get a glimpse of the man. Husbands, she knew, intrigued them; the children didn't recognize their own fathers as husbands. Their fathers were fathers, no more, no less. Husbands existed in fairy tales, in commercials, in grocery stores, and now, in their teacher's drawing.

"A . . . telemarketer," she said, though she'd meant to say "paramedic."

"What's that?" asked Glenna.

"It's a man who sells things on the phone." She paused. "He works from home. He doesn't have to go to an office. It's hard for him to leave the house. People always want to talk to him because he's very handsome. He is also very tall. And sometimes he picks me up and carries me into restaurants. And we order dessert first."

Ralph blinked, then rested a chin in his hand. "He could probably wrestle."

She elongated the figure's arm, connecting it to the palm of the other figure so that its shape eclipsed the shovel's handle. "He *could* probably wrestle," she said, realizing that her legs had fallen asleep and realizing, too, that she didn't care.

By lunch time, news of her husband had traveled from the Coloring Table to the Numbers Booth, from the Reading Carpet to the Animal Center. Even Archer Fleece seemed to swim with greater enthusiasm, excited by the room's palpable energy. In the Puppet Corner, Melvin placed a zebra on his arm and said, "*I am a husband!*"

In the afternoon, after the children had departed in the arms of anxious mothers or half-empty school buses, she stood over the Coloring Table and collected the drawings. She could, she knew, toss her own drawing in the trash, letting it mingle with milk cartons and tissues and apple cores. But it seemed a different thing, not ready to meet its end. It seemed alive, like a Post-It note marked with the name of a restaurant she intended to visit. She placed her drawing on the bulletin board next to Anna's drawing of her family, a drawing with green arrows pointing to five purple stick figures.

On Thursday, she meant to avoid the Coloring Table. She meant to focus on the Numbers Booth and to teach Gerald, the suspected genius, about prime numbers, but the children at the Coloring Table—seven students this time—raised their hands into the air and called her name, saying, "Draw more! Draw more!"

She drew a house, calling it "our house." She described the stainless-steel appliances, saying they looked like jewelry in the right light. "Before I met my husband," she said, "I had a plastic coffee maker. Can you imagine?"

The children laughed, their sounds a theme song for second-rate objects.

She used words that confused but enchanted their tiny ears: *trellis, landscape architect, storm windows, wall-to-wall carpeting, five-hundred thread count.* They asked questions about backyard gardens and whirlpools and refrigerators stocked with ice cream sandwiches. She said yes, yes to everything, denying nothing. Her words lived only in the affirmative, confirming the children's greatest hopes, materializing their deepest desires. She said she loved the house, said they'd lived there since the nineties.

"The nineties?" Glenna asked at Story Hour.

She'd meant to read *Hansel and Gretel*, but they'd encouraged her to put down the book and *tell more* about the house, the husband, the garden with the ice sculptures and karaoke machine.

"I was married in the nineties," she said. "I don't even remember what life was like before I was married. I got married *before* you were *born*."

A collective gasp came up from the circle. Anna clutched at Glenna's braid. Dale bit his lip. The children marveled at any person or object delivered from a decade they'd missed.

During morning recess, she watched the children from the window, sprinkled tiny flakes of fish food onto the surface of the water surrounding Archer Fleece, and told herself it did not matter. The life she relayed, it meant something. To them, not her. It made them hopeful, hopeful about the world, about adulthood, about how life would unfold in front of them, miles of wishes granted and deserved objects received. The other facts, the ones associated with her life, would make them fear the world. They'd recoil at the sight of her single, solitary stick figure on the page, weighed down by the space around it. They were too young to think lonely existed. Let them think it a myth, she thought, and considered buying a companion for Archer Fleece.

On Friday, she brought in a framed photo and placed it on her desk during snack time.

"This is *him*," she said to her students. She brought in the photo for them, not for her. She wanted them to know he watched over them like a velvet angel on top of a Christmas tree. She'd decided it wasn't enough for them to know of him; they had to see him, though of course they weren't seeing *him*. They were seeing a photo of her high school Biology teacher, which she'd cut from an old yearbook. At seventeen, she had loved him in the faulty, dull way one loves a teacher. She'd wanted to wear his lab coat, that much she remembered, even after he said she was "overbearing, well, not overbearing, but almost." He'd warned her about adulthood, said she wouldn't be able to "elbow her way into it." She let Anna kiss the photo.

"He's handsome like a prince," Anna had said, studying the blurry mark her lips had left across the glass. Her eyes widened at a sudden thought. "Handsome like a prince from *Russia*."

This was the highest compliment. The children had recently learned of Russia, finding it on the inflatable globe and trusting in its open, full form. They perpetually posed questions about Russia. Dale had asked to be nicknamed Russia. Glenna had asked to revise her career goal, throwing *Make staircases* in the trash, and replacing it with *Go to Russia every day*.

She knelt down, putting a hand on Anna's shoulder. "Anna, I'm going to tell you something. And only you, okay?"

Anna gave the solemn nod of a favored student. Anna was, of course, the favorite one, the one she'd choose if she could have any of them because of course teachers thought about this, imagining parents distributing the children like Halloween candy.

"He *lived* in Russia," she said. "And he *visits* Russia. In the spring." She put a finger to her lips. "But don't tell the others."

At this, Anna threw her arms around her neck, marking the first hug she'd received from a tiny set of rail-thin arms.

Over the weekend, her mind went elsewhere when her hands reached for lettuce at the grocery store, when her arms scrubbed mildew from the shower walls, when her eyes looked over the pages of the magazine the postman had left in her mailbox though it should have been delivered to the woman in the apartment next door, Mrs. Kelve, the therapist Baptist or Baptist therapist (she couldn't remember the order of things). Her brain took a walk through the realm of verbal possibility, stopping to look at each statement, inspecting it like a new car. On Monday, she'd tell the children that they'd honeymooned in Greece and that he was *good with numbers*. She'd wear her best shirt and say he *picked it up* for her. She'd paint her nails, say he preferred that color. She'd hum a tune, say it was his favorite, the one he sang before he proposed in a bakery in front of a cake that looked just like the one they'd chosen for their wedding.

On Monday, she brought leftovers in a small Tupperware dish and held it up in front of the children. "We do not cook for two," she announced. "We cook for many." The children nodded attentively when she explained the notion of a candle-lit dinner.

On Tuesday, the Coloring Table commissioned a series of drawings called *Super Mr. Til*. Dale drew him holding a gun made from ice cream. Anna drew him riding a dragon into a swimming pool. Glenna simply wrote the word *KISS* across the paper, circling it with a large, grey heart, and dangling stars from the tip of each S.

On Wednesday, she brought in her prom dress—she hadn't been to the prom, of course she hadn't been to the prom, but a neighbor had given her the dress anyway saying, "Every girl needs sparkling touches"— and said, "This is *the* dress!" The children cheered and formed a line to touch the sequins around the waist, the satin, the segmented line of thread pressed against the hem. Even Anna, Anna who hated pink, Anna who wanted to be interesting, Anna would understood the precise and imperfect rejection of normalcy, said, "It's like a *movie* dress."

They asked and she told. She told all day. They asked about his childhood, his siblings, his brave but brief career as a fighter pilot. She told until the afternoon, when the guidance counselor, Mr. Harvey, a small, elderly man no taller than a mailbox at the end of a driveway, arrived to deliver the first of his bi-weekly guidance lessons.

"They're looking a little glassy-eyed," Mr. Harvey said, approaching her desk as the children took their seats at the tables. "Did they just have a snack?"

"Yes," she said. "They did." This wasn't a lie. What was a story if not a snack? A story offered nourishment, promise, energy.

"A sleepy face doesn't worry me," he said, winking. "That's the only face my wife ever makes," and as he walked towards the front of the classroom, she imagined his wife, Mrs. Harvey, a grey woman who wore ill-fitting cardigans and placed spoonfuls of soggy peas on her husband's plate each night at dinner.

Mr. Harvey stood next to the cheetah poster, unknowingly positioning himself so that it looked as though the cheetah were about to pounce on his head. "I'm Mr. Harvey," he said, addressing the children with a small, thin smile. "I'm a *new* visitor to this classroom. I'm a *new* friend to you, and you're a *new* friend to me. I think it's important to get to know your new friends. Today, I'm going to learn about you. We're going to do an activity that lets *me* find out about *you*." He then instructed the students—her students—to draw pictures of themselves doing any activity that they liked to do.

As they retrieved crayons from the coffee cans and began to draw, she watched from her desk in the corner. She felt far away, unknown and unseen. She felt as though she'd lost them. She wanted to shout an addendum to Mr. Harvey's request, asking the children to do something else, to draw a certain shape across the top of their page, exclamation points or squiggles, a sort of code that said, *We're hers.*

But this, she told herself, was simply what it felt like to momentarily lose a thing, to have it take on a new life in front of you. Perhaps the parents felt this each morning as they moved their children from their cars to her classroom.

She stared at him as he walked around the room, conversing with the children and asking them about their drawings. He stopped by Anna's chair and peered at her work.

"What are *you* doing in your drawing?" asked Mr. Harvey.

"I'm sewing a sweater for Desperado, my cat," she responded.

"Mmm. Well, it looks like you're holding him on your lap *and* sewing."

"I'm sewing it *on* him," she said.

"Well." Mr. Harvey's response did not extend beyond this word. He returned to the front of the room. "Now, my *new* friends, I want you to find someone in the room who made a drawing that shows them doing the *same activity* that you're doing in *your* drawing."

In a matter of seconds, the students became visibly frustrated, unable to find a drawing that matched their own. Ralph put his hand against his forehead and began shaking his head. Anna stood, hand on hips, saying to Glenna, "But you have a cat so why didn't you *draw* the cat?" Gerald shrugged and turned to Patrick. "It's hard to draw a Rubik's cube, but I did it."

"Alright, alright!" said Mr. Harvey, clapping his hands. "Let's all have a seat."

"But no one drew what I drew!" said Glenna, holding up her paper. "I drew me making fruit salad and nobody drew anybody making fruit salad!"

"I *know*," said Mr. Harvey. "And I know you *feel* frustrated. But why do you feel frustrated?" He walked towards her and put a hand on her shoulder, then guided her towards her chair. "Do we *all* need to draw the same *thing*? Isn't it *okay* that our pictures are different? Isn't it *okay* that we are all *different*?" He looked at Glenna. "Isn't it okay?"

She stared at her drawing and shrugged. "I just like fruit salad."

He beamed, as though her words had been a compliment directed towards him. "We *all* do different things, but that's o*kay* because we're all different. But when I see what you drew, I learn about you! And I love to learn about you. If I made a drawing, you'd learn about me, and you'd learn why we're different. If Ms. Til made a drawing, you'd learn about her."

"She did make a drawing," said Anna, pointing towards the bulletin board. "It's right there!"

"She drew *Mr.* Til," said Dale.

"Mr. Til?" asked Mr. Harvey.

Her Meat Face. It appeared as though on command, without warning, with insistence, surely deeper and redder than ever before.

"We don't even need the drawing anymore because she brought in a picture," said Ralph, motioning towards the framed photo on her desk.

She looked from the framed photo to Mr. Harvey. Mr. Harvey, the man she'd met at in-service. Mr. Harvey, the man she often saw in the parking lot. Mr. Harvey, the man who knew the words "Mr. Til" did not have a physical equivalent.

"Well." Again, the landscape of one word to indicate the entire continent of reaction. "I think we're done," he said, smiling and looking down at the children. "You, my new friends, get to go out for recess, and I'll see *you* next time."

After the children had formed a line, Mr. Harvey opened the door and the students rushed past him onto the playground. They brought with them their noise and movement so that when they were gone, the room took on the familiar, eerie silence of a place once occupied by children.

"Karen," he said. "May I see that photo?"

She took the photo from her desk, stood up, and held out the photo, a peace offering, a smoking gun, a confession, a knock-knock joke.

"Who is this?" he said, taking the photo from her without looking at it.

"My husband," she said.

"I wasn't aware of your marriage. You don't wear a ring, and you've never made mention of him before."

"Well," she replied, her mouth readying for another lie, the easy, good concoction. "I *was* married."

"So this is your . . . *ex*-husband?"

"Yes," she said, marveling at the quick-fire magic of false assumptions.

"So he's not *really* your husband?" he asked.

"Well, not legally," she said. "But *emotionally*, you know . . . I'm still attached."

"Karen," he said, sighing. "Your attachment is your business, not your *students'* business."

"That's not true," she replied. "He is their business. He's important to them."

He raised a grey eyebrow. "Important?"

"They need him. They need him in the way they need Santa Claus."

"They don't 'need' Santa Claus, per se," he said. "Santa Claus was provided to them by somebody. Santa Claus does not meet a need."

"Well, then, they like him." She paused. "And I think we should let them keep him."

At this, Mr. Harvey crossed his arms, pinning the photo against his chest. "No. We won't be doing that."

"What would it hurt?" she asked, because she did not know.

"It would hurt your accountability. *Our* accountability. If a parent asks about him and they discover you've presented your *ex*-husband as your *husband*, we're all going to be accountable. It will make them wonder what other misrepresentations are floating around this school. What if your students ask to meet him? What if you run into one of the families at the post office and they ask you where he is? It starts with *the children's* questions and ends with the *parents'* questions."

"That won't happen."

"It might. And what will you do then?" He paused, then spoke in a suspiciously soothing voice. "Is it *embarrassment*, Karen?"

It wasn't embarrassment. Of course it wasn't embarrassment. But she'd lost its name. If she knew the name, she'd wish it into her mouth.

"You don't *need* to be embarrassed, not in front of them, not in front of me, not in front of anybody. They couldn't care less, *we* couldn't care less, whether you're married or divorced or single, whether you've got a gaggle of kids or a houseplant." He motioned towards the playground. "Those children want honesty, just like everyone else."

"How do you know that's what everybody wants?" she asked, because maybe he knew, because maybe everybody knew what everybody wanted, because maybe there'd been a meeting and maybe she'd missed it and here she stood wanting what everyone else had decided against wanting.

He blinked at her and cocked his head. "Because who wouldn't want honesty?" He smiled the same small, thin smile he'd worn when facing her students. "Honesty has a certain *thrill* to it, you know." He took the photo frame and held it in front of him, finally looking at the image within it. "A doctor?" he asked, handing it back to her.

"A biology teacher," she said flatly.

"Well." He stared at her for a moment. "Just try honesty, ok? Think of it like, I don't know, a new *red jacket* or something. It might feel *good*. When the kids get back here, tell them the truth. Tell them that this man is no longer in your life and take that photo off of your desk. We want to be sure that everyone's clear. They'll accept it, and move on to something else." He began walking towards the door. "We'll keep this between us, of course. Unless it's not . . . *handled*. Then we'll have to tell others. But I assume you'll handle it because I know you can *handle* things." He winked at her before disappearing into the hallway.

When he was gone, she walked over to the window and stood in front of Archer Fleece. She watched him swim the length of the bowl, then back again. She turned her gaze towards the children outside. They occupied every corner of the playground, their bodies marking their favored territories. Anna played hopscotch with Glenna. Gerald stood beneath the monkey bars. Dale offered Ralph a high-five by the jungle gym.

Tell them, Mr. Harvey had said.

But what to tell them?

She could make drawings, drawings of the tiny apartment, the threadbare couch, the musty closet, the refrigerator that made the strange noise each evening like chickens were at its backside. She could tell them of her brothers, of her father, of the impossibility of strangers, of how *meet* is a four-letter word, complicated like geometry and rough as sandpaper. She could tell them that bodies used to be beside her, but bodies disappear in instants, in years, in the slow progression of weeks and months. She could tell them that things were difficult for her, some for good reason, others for no reason at all. She could tell them that it had felt good to say those squat, tight words: *him, ours.* She could tell them she'd marveled at how thick and good her life became when elevated to something told rather than something lived.

She looked down at Archer Fleece and remembered her plan to buy him a mate. She'd forgotten her intention; it had left her like breath. She scooped him up from the water and examined him in her hand, his tail swaying back and forth against the unfamiliar territory of her palm.

His motion startled her. She had expected him, she realized, to curl up on her skin like a kitten in her lap. She had expected him to like it there, with her, outside his space. She had expected him to nuzzle her palm, to purr, or to stretch. She resented the wide eyes and the swishing tail that told her he was unfamiliar with kindness, suspicious of nurture. She resented his gaze, the way he looked at her as if he didn't know her, as if she hadn't seen this gaze before, as though she would not see it, would not feel it.

She stuffed him into her mouth, not for her, but for them, because what if he looked at children like that? What if they learned the feeling of being unknown? In a gulp, he was delivered into her stomach, a rush of scales and silk down her throat.

From within her, he would, perhaps, raise his eyes upwards to see her throat. He would, perhaps, watch the words leave her body, linked together like the children when lining up for recess, *I* and *am* and *alone*. But it wouldn't be true; she would be occupied by something, though it was small, no bigger than a pack of chewing gum, a thing once known, then claimed, and when the children returned to find him gone, she'd say, *He's here, but you just can't see him.* ❧

www.noonannual.com

J.R. Ackerley's MY FATHER AND MYSELF

Dave Madden

I might never write a memoir. Looking into the murk of one's past and seeing in there a story to tell has always seemed a kind of magic to me, like the Wicked Queen's conjuring from her mirror on the wall a sooth-sayer to tell her, for certain, what's what. I grew up white and middle-class in the suburbs to parents who worked jobs and are still together. I had no accent, no noteworthy heritage, no local cuisine, no troubled siblings, no friends who died. I got good grades and did extracurriculars. I went to college and then I went to graduate school.

Even I'm not interested in this story; no amount of craft could make it palatable to a stranger.

Trouble, growing up, happened to other people, and when I became a writer and made writer friends, memoir is what other writers got to work on. I'd be an asshole if I wrote here that I envied them their troubles, their lives that they survived and then wrote into to try to understand just how that survival happened. Everybody works from the material they have. But I hope not to be an asshole when I write that I envied them the gifts of attention their memoir projects granted. It's a cliché (also wrong) to say that writing memoir is like therapy, but I've been in therapy long enough now to see how a sustained inquiry into who I've been could only help in my task to understand who I am.

I thought it was something left for other people until I read J.R. Ack-erley's *My Father and Myself* last Christmas. Here's its opening:

> I was born in 1896 and my parents were married in 1919. Nearly a quarter of a century may seem rather procrastinatory for making up one's mind, but I expect that the longer such rites are postponed the less indispensable they appear and that, as the years rolled by, my parents gradually forgot the anomaly of their situation.

You can hear the voice. Fussy, prudent. Who says "rather procrastina-tory" or "the anomaly of their situation"? Who but a queer would lean so pansily on such Latinate constructions?

This queer. I raise my hand and place myself among those writers who struggle to keep things Anglo-Saxon, the way Ernest Hemingway learned to from Sherwood Anderson, and the way I learned to from read-ing angry George Orwell in graduate school. I also struggle with Henry James's scenic method, taught as gospel everywhere ever since the Iowa Writers' Workshop opened its doors. My nature is to tell, not show, because the world has always presented itself to be as a problem to be solved through rumination and analysis, not a pageantry of sensory data to be channeled onto the page.

Here, too, I found in Ackerley a fellow traveler. The almost Teutonic literalness of its title gives you an idea of the memoir's focus: Ackerley spends eighteen chapters (plus appendix) looking at his own life and what he knows of the life of his father, to understand not just the nature of their relationship but the nature of their selves. *How am I a part of whoever the man my father was?* is a central question. Ackerley fought in the Battle of the Somme, and seems among the members of his battalion to've been one of the few survivors. Here's how that gets rendered in chapter seven:

> Many of the officers in my battalion were struck down the moment they emerged into view. My company commander was shot through the heart before he had advanced a step. Neville, the battalion buffoon . . . was also instantly killed, and so was fat Bobby Soames, my best friend. I had spent the previous evening with him and he had said to me quietly, without emotion, "I am going to be killed tomorrow. I don't know how I know it but I do."

Despite what it says, it's itself not without emotion, the passage. What it is without is an interest in manufacturing emotion by using the tools of narrative. We're given no scene of Bobby and J.R. talking on the eve of battle, no image of his best friend's face looming adumbratively at the end of a chapter. The detail is told at the exact moment, so it feels, it arrives in Ackerley's sorting brain, and in doing this for more than 200 pages, *My Father and Myself* is the most nonfictive memoir I've ever read.

A memoir that's like a novel except true is no better than a mirror on the wall that won't rank your beauty. That only reflects back to you the face you show to it. If I ever wrote a memoir, I'd want it to tell me something, not show me what it is I can remember. I'm afraid, probably, of narrative. Every time I turn myself into a literary character, with arcs and demonstrable desires, that self becomes even more alien to me. Any idiot can see that writing a memoir is an act of great courage. Keeping myself an essaying narrator has always felt like cowardice. And then I read Ackerley. I might still be a coward, but now I don't feel as lonely. ❧

Yellow Snow

Tom Treanor

Nights I sleep warm, sweaty sleep. The kind of sleep that brings with it a week of illness. The kind of illness that lingers, travels from one residency specialty to the next: GI, respiratory, ear nose and throat. I can feel it in my chest. Sputum like driveway gravel.

It is January and we've had a week of summertime. No marine layer since the Christmas sales. The rest of the country is in the deep freeze, but here we've landed Indian summer.

I call Clairebear. She lives where it snows.

"I'm getting sick," I tell her.

She recommends multivitamins, unfiltered cranberry juice, dietary supplements that effervesce.

"What ever happened to chicken soup?"

She says there have been studies on zinc. There are lozenges, cherry-flavored.

"They're disgusting," I say to her. "They make my mouth taste like dimes."

She says last year the snow didn't stick at all. This year, it's everywhere. On cars, fire escapes, awnings and umbrellas, picnic tables in the backyards. It looks so different the way the city lights at night descend upon everything from the reflection in the sky, how the snow glows like pink twilight: it's emanating, a slow burn, it's the mothership coming in for a landing.

The date breaks a votive on the table with her purse. Wax spews. It was an accident; she says she could use a drink. She just moved back after a year in Belize, but that's not her excuse.

"What does one do in Belize for a year?" I ask her.

One apprentices as a personal chef to a billionaire with a compound of jungle bungalows. She says it was a learning experience.

"What did you learn to cook?" I ask her.

Cheeseburgers, of all kinds.

"All one of them?"

No smile on her end, and I laugh a kind of stupid snicker. A first-date snicker.

She orders a double bourbon.

A man wearing a hospital gown jostles open the doors to reception and pisses on the floor. It is early; reception is not yet open. The doors, apparently, were unlocked. We watch from the security monitors bolted above the switchboard, all in fisheye black-and-white. The man moves the couch to cover the spot on the floor. He sits on the couch, pisses on the couch. We aren't sure who we should call first: the police or facilities management.

The chief security officer is a woman months shy of retirement. Ruthie Basso, former cop, wears Christmas sweaters. She says the man was not dangerous, just confused, unwell, smelled like a septic tank. He was looking for his wife.

"Who is his wife?" I ask her.

He didn't know. He thought he might find her here.

I wake up into what feels like a pressurized fog. Sitting up in bed, the room goes hyperbolic. I think fever: feed a fever, starve a cold. Or is it the opposite?

Daylight is bright, searing, prying open the sky into something bigger and bluer than is meant to be. People strut the streets in shorts and t-shirts and tangerine swimwear, taunting with their flip-flops the rainy season gone on vacation.

Insects have been swarming the neighborhood. Bees, flies, bugs with wings and nubby segmented bodies. They say it's the warm weather. They say the insects have nowhere else to go. Bees everywhere, their nests nestled in the eaves of Victorians. So many competing for shelter, searching for hives. So in my kitchen, they've come to die: a tiny, perfect pile like a cone of sand in an hourglass. Here they are, a dish of desiccated bees, with their fuzzy carcasses and vellum wings, a pyramid of puffed wheat.

I cancel a date because I blow bloody mucus into a napkin. The advice nurse on the telephone tells me I am at the peak of illness. It's only gonna get better from here on out.

"Is there some kind of tea I should be drinking?" I ask her. "Herbal tea?"

Orange juice, she recommends. Fluids, water, unfiltered cranberry juice.

"I'm really quite interested in the tea," I say to her. I ask about naturopathy, homeopathy, aromatherapy. "I understand that frankincense costs a hundred bucks for a vial the size of a diary key."

She's unfamiliar. I should be tip-top in no time. It's just something that's going around. And for one hundred dollars, she'd rather go out for a nice steak.

Back in the office, three days out sick. The receptionist has been fired. She forgot to lock the doors again. Apparently it was a pattern. She had been monitored, she had been performance planned. They said it was a statement: forgetfulness, disobedience, insubordination.

I'm told I still sound hoarse. I say, "But I'm no Mister Ed!"

They hired professionals to steam-clean the carpets. They selected new couches from catalogues.

Another date, two weeks after the last. This girl a former Peace Corps volunteer. The Ukraine. Extended tour, back just in September. Taught English language classes on a potato farm.

"Is potato farm a fancy way of saying vodka distillery?" I ask her.

No, a potato farm is a potato farm.

Those who go overseas have their lives changed. They return world-weary and important. They wouldn't trade it for anything. This girl practically learned Russian overnight, a special dialectic Slavic. A whole new alphabet of potato, tuber, root.

"My friend Clairebear lived in the South Pacific for two years," I say to her. "The Marshall Islands. Got a plantar wart the size of a frisbee. Foot surgery in Honolulu, the works."

The date orders a bourbon. I consider one too.

Vodka in the States, she scoffs. She won't touch the stuff.

Clairebear calls and says she's never seen so much snow in her neighborhood. She is in love. Snow collects in powdery haloes in the windows of brownstones.

Snow brings out my inner child. I make snow angels, snowballs, snowmen and their families. Snowmistresses, the occasional illegitimate snowbaby. It's been maybe years since I've even seen snow. Clairebear and I, together then with a boulder of packed snow, pushing it down a leaf-littered slope. The snowball was large, the way refrigerators and sofas are large, not quite spherical, not quite cubic, gathered like peeling up fresh tongues of sod from a lawn.

People here are going to the beach, working on their winter tan.

"I wish I could be there," I say to her. "To play in the snow."

Clairebear asks how the last date went.

"I have a new appreciation for American whiskeys," I say to her.

That good? she asks.

Since sickness, I haven't slept. Several nights now of tossing, turning, sheets wrung and twisted. I am convinced I should take something. My medicine cabinet is lined with over-the-counter sleep-aids in squat bottles, and I tell the advice nurse on the telephone that they don't work.

"It's just been so warm," I say to her.

Her phone voice hits a caramel timber on par with twenty years of cigarettes. I should see a GP, she tells me. Try something prescription-strength. There are anxiety repressors, time-release capsules. Sedatives, some of the best used as antidepressants in extremely high does.

"If that were the case," I ask her, "wouldn't I be asleep all the time?"

Exactly.

"I was really sick last week," I say to her. I search for redemption, for sleep-starved validation. "I have a post-nasal drip that goes drip drip drip."

I wonder if the advice nurse has ever had to talk people through plague. The Hanta virus, Ebola, something flesh-eating, tubercular, exoticized from the common cold. Spanish flu, avian flu, flu of the drug-resistant variety, eating vaccines for breakfast. I am not sure how to broach the subject.

"Can you coach how to perform a testicular self-exam?" I ask her.

One bee buzzes aside the dusty corner of the windowsill. It moves like a marionette.

Reception smells plastic. The carpet has been spray-tinted, walls painted anew. Things glisten a fire-retardant gloss.

The new girl in reception is a germaphobe. We watch her from the switchboard as she arranges magazines on the tables. Back issues are spun into perfect pinwheels. She snaps on purple nitrile gloves before she handles anything. She suggests placing the front desk behind plate glass.

A tiny doorbell is fitted to the underside of her desk in case of another incident clad in a hospital gown. She used to work in a bank. Ruthie Basso's number is on speed-dial.

People at work are dropping like flies. They're detoxing on cocktails of vitamins, dining on flights of antibiotics. My supervisor has gone nasal, calls me Patient Zero.

Accidentally, I knock over a wastebasket in the hallway on my way to the restroom. Wadded tissues scatter like errant snowballs.

New date, this time a girl with charisma to spare. Nonchalance as flirtation. She's just getting over something. A nasty cough, but no more; tissues are at the ready. Hasn't been out of the country since a senior trip in high school. Europe, the ABC tour: Another Boring Church.

"Bourbon?" I offer.

In Europe, her group scheduled only an hour for the Louvre. An hour! Other kids wanted to do other things. Other kids, the temper-tantrum toddlers, complained, stomped their feet; museums are *bor*-ing, they said. She and her friends weren't going to be daunted; determined, they ran through the whole place. Floor by marble floor, sweeping the halls to the tick of a stopwatch. Like a race, like a gameshow.

"Mona Lisa?"

She nods.

"Venus de Milo?"

She nods.

"Even Winged Victory?"

And all that wingspan, she says to me, doesn't do you a bit of good without a head.

Clairebear's voice falls when she sees the ten-day forecast. No new scheduled snowfall, just Antarctic cold.

I say to her, "No more yellow snow."

No, she huffs. Only green ribbons of frozen dog piss.

And I picture it perfectly, snaked in kinks down the concrete.

My first night of deep sleep, and I'm woken up to the click click of rain. A deluge, the oscillating rush of rain on the roof, like an amniotic slosh, hitting hard like a heartbeat.

With the first scissor of thunder, I make a beeline to the window.

People are dancing. They're drenched and screeching, holding their hands up into yellow streetlamp light where the rain glows like laser beams. The streets on the hills run like rivers. The ground is pinched tight, happy with its dryness, the water with nowhere to go. And it's only just begun. ❧

Index

The following is a listing in alphabetical order by author's last name of works published in *Post Road*. An asterisk indicates subject rather than contributor.